Sex Toys

Putting the BOOM back in boomers

Dear Sharon,

Enjoy the read.

Dr. Burda

Sex Toys

Putting the BOOM back in boomers

By

Dr. Brenda Dressler

Illustrated by

Julia Drelich

Jari Books
Boynton Beach, Florida

Published in the United States by Jari Books, P.O.Box 741871, Boynton Beach, Fl 33437.

Printed in the United States
Book cover: Ray Bossik

Disclaimer
Information and recommendations provided in this book are intended to help the reader make healthy choices. This book is not designed to be a replacement for a physician. Confer with your physician for a diagnosis and treatment of a medical nature. The author disclaims any liability should the information be incorrect or incomplete. All information contained in this book is "as is" and the author makes no guarantees or assurances about the book's contents. The author will not be held responsible or liable for damages or negative consequences resulting from following suggestions provided in this book.

The appendices provide additional information for the consumer and are not intended to indicate endorsement of any sex toy companies, personal lubricants, sex stores (online or retail) including, but not limited to, stores targeting feminists and the LGBTQIAP+ community. Additionally, references are listed to provide sources of information and are not intended to endorse any websites or books. Readers should be aware that websites mentioned in this book may not be active in the future.

ISBN: 978-0-578-88813-2 (paperback)
ISBN: 978-0-578-90444-3 (ebook)

Library of Congress Control Number: 2021908438

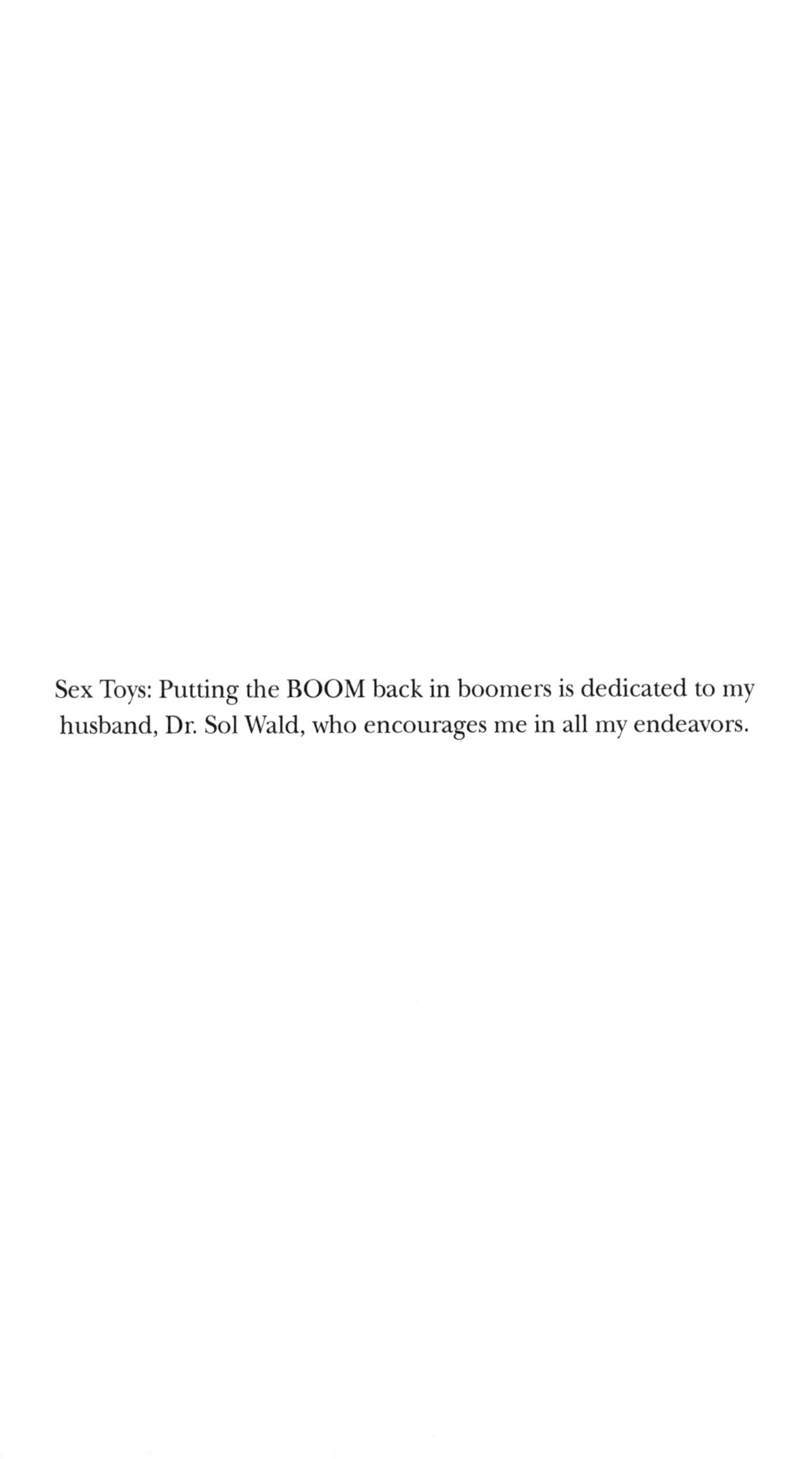

Sex Toys: Putting the BOOM back in boomers is dedicated to my husband, Dr. Sol Wald, who encourages me in all my endeavors.

Contents

Tables

Illustrations

Introduction

While writing a book on sex for people over the age of 60, I found that my interest in sex toys was piqued. I was surprised to learn that they aren't regulated by any governmental agency and cause more serious injuries than children's toys. The U.S. Food and Drug Administration (FDA) regards pleasure toys as novelty items. The Consumer Protection Safety Commission (CPSC) requires manufacturers of adult toys to follow compliance laws for its electronic parts. Many pleasure toys imported from China are made with toxic chemicals. That's why I put my book, *Sex Beyond 60: Myths and Facts*, aside to research and write this book devoted entirely to the subject of pleasure toys.

Pleasure toys provide many benefits. Adults are aroused by toys during solo or partner sex. Pleasure toys and sex furniture encourage playfulness and intimacy, and assist people with disabilities. They are an excellent alternative to medication. For example, physicians sometimes recommend vibrators to women to increase vaginal lubrication and to women who don't orgasm during sex.

Orgasms provide many health benefits. Some men are able to orgasm with masturbation sleeves. Some physicians recommend that men get a prostate massage as an alternative to drug treatment, and men claim that prostate orgasms are exquisite. This book provides instructions for giving yourself or a partner a prostate massage, which can be done manually or with an anal toy.

The popularity of sex toys is reflected in a steadily increasing demand. Baby boomers, who came of age during the sexual revolution in the 1960s, drive sales of pleasure toys and personal lubricants. U.S. consumers spent about $9 billion on pleasure toys in 2020 and about $219 million on personal lubricants in 2018. During the COVID-19 pandemic, when many people were isolated, demand for pleasure toys tripled, and sex toy manufacturers profited tremendously.

The FDA regulates personal lubricants as Class II medical devices because pleasure toys and personal lubricants are used internally. The dilemma is that there are several types of lubricants and many brands of these products. But you might ask yourself: 'Which one can a baby boomer safely use, and which one is safe for use with pleasure toys?' This book will answer those questions for you.

At New York University I studied human sexuality and earned a doctorate in Health Education in 1986. In 1987, I was certified by the American Association of Sex Educators, Counselors, and Therapists (AASECT) and currently maintain membership in this organization. In 1989, I was certified by the American Board of Sexology and also became a certified health education specialist (CHES).

For the past 50 years, I have taught sexuality education to students in middle school, high school, college, and universities in New York, Israel, and Uganda. As Comprehensive Health Coordinator of Queens, I trained New York City public school administrators and faculty how to teach sex education. I also taught them how to identify and report suspected child abuse, and I educated them about child sexual abuse prevention, sexuality and disability, and HIV/AIDS prevention, including the Condom Availability Program. At Queens high schools, HIV/AIDS prevention education teams affectionately called me The Condom Queen of Queens.

While researching sex toy companies, I found little or no information about the materials used in pleasure toys and how to clean and store them. Some sex toy companies use confusing terminology. For example, I've seen ten different terms to describe silicone, a material used in pleasure toys. Some toy companies also use food-grade silicone and label their packages "body safe" or "medical grade." Overall, some of these companies use misleading product information online and on product packaging.

When the erotic novel, *Fifty Shades of Grey* was published in 2011, sales of anal beads, butt plugs, Ben-Wa balls, prostate massagers, vibrators, dildos, and handcuffs soared. The Consumer Product Safety Commission reported that injuries from pleasure toys doubled since the publication of the book. The majority of these injuries were a result of design flaws occurring in the anorectal region. Pleasure toys with sharp sides may cause cuts and tears. Vibrators and other adult toys that have electronic parts can expose the user to dangerous wiring and shocks. Vibratory strain injury is a condition of chronic numbness and pain over time is caused by vibrations. In addition to these design errors, many pleasure toys contain dangerous chemicals.

Consumers need help avoiding pleasure toys that contain toxic materials and dangerous design errors. And consumers may be uneasy about asking an adult toy salesperson about a pleasure toy's material and its correct usage. *Sex Toys: Putting the BOOM back in boomers* will show you how to select a body-safe pleasure toy that is perfect for you.

You probably have many questions about pleasure toys. You may be wondering how to suggest the use of these toys to your partner. You may also want to know what to do if your partner is resistant to the idea. This book will give you strategies to make your partner comfortable with the idea of using pleasure toys with you.

In *Sex Toys: Putting the BOOM back in boomers,* I recommend safe, pleasurable toys for older adults. You'll find descriptions, illustrations, and approximate prices of these toys to help you make an informed decision. Important information is summarized in the tables and appendices. Appendix A contains sex-positive retail adult sex stores that target feminists, couples, and the LGBTQIAP+ (lesbian, gay, bisexual, transgender, queer or questioning, intersex, asexual, and pansexual+ {+meaning "not limited to") community. Brick-and-mortar sex shops that sell various size dildos are listed in Appendix B. Retail adult stores that sell body-safe pleasure toys are listed in Appendix C. Reputable sex toy manufacturers can be found in Appendix D. Appendix E contains information about personal lubricants compiled by the World Health Organization and other researchers. Appendix F is a compilation of pleasure toys for baby boomers.

You'll find answers to all your questions in *Sex Toys: Putting the BOOM back in boomers.* Then go shopping and have fun.

Visit my website at www.brendadressler.com.

CHAPTER 1

Myths and Facts about Pleasure Toys

In 1998, the TV series, *Sex and the City*, featured the rabbit vibrator. In the episode, "The Turtle and the Hare," the show's foursome — Carrie, Samantha, Miranda, and Charlotte — talked about orgasms experienced with the nine-inch pink rabbit vibrator. As a result, this pleasure toy became a pop culture sensation. Female shoppers went to adult sex stores to buy the vibrator, which sold out the day after the *Sex and the City* episode aired.[1]

Pleasure toys have now gone mainstream. Target, Walmart, CVS, and other retail stores sell them. The Museum of Modern Art (MOMA) Design Store and the Museum of Sex, both located in NYC, affirm sex positivity and sell pleasure toys and personal lubricants. Wirecutter, a division of the New York Times that reviews consumer products, now includes the best vibrators for 2020.

However, myths about pleasure toys continue to influence beliefs, preventing some people from experimenting with them.

Is it true that pleasure toys are for single or lonely people?

No. Research in the United States provides evidence that pleasuring yourself with an adult toy doesn't interfere with enjoying sex and intimacy with a partner.

America is in the midst of a sexual revolution, and there's ample evidence to prove it. For example, in 2009, over 50 percent of women who ranged in age from 18 to 60 and used vibrators while in a relationship reported more desire, arousal, lubrication, and orgasms.[2] About 50 percent of married and single women use vibrators in sex play.[3]

A survey of 2,056 women ages 14 to 94 was completed in 2010. About 52 percent of the participants reported masturbating with a vibrator when alone and during penetrative sex with a partner.[4] Approximately 65 percent of women owned vibrators in 2017.[5] Vibrators, lubricants, and dildos are frequently part of sex play for heterosexual, lesbian, and bisexual women.[6] A 2010 study revealed that 45 percent of 1,022 heterosexual men used vibrators during foreplay and during sexual intercourse.[7]

Does a vibrator desensitize the body?

No. A vibrator provides stronger stimulation than the fingers and hands and doesn't reduce sensitivity.

Do people only use vibrators for masturbation?

No. Besides being used for masturbation, vibrators can enhance foreplay and oral and sexual intercourse, as well as stimulating the prostate gland.

Is something wrong with women who use vibrators to climax?

No. About 25 percent of sexually-normal females in the United States require more stimulation than can be provided by the fingers or tongue.[8] Women can be aroused and sexually satisfied by vibrators.

Are gay men the only ones who use anal pleasure toys?

No. Some straight men associate anal stimulation with gay men. Research on heterosexuals in 2010 revealed that 51 percent of men and 43 percent of women engaged in oral and anal sex, manual-anal sex, or inserted an anal toy.[9] In 2015, a study reported that 71 percent of heterosexual men in a relationship wanted a prostate massage. About 80 percent of women were interested in giving it.[10]

Does a vibrator make you lose interest in a sex partner?

No. Any suggestion to that effect is a myth. Vibrators help many adult women achieve lubrication and orgasm faster while strengthening muscles and nerve pathways. Pleasure toys aren't a substitute for intimacy with a partner, though.

Can people who have weak relationships benefit from pleasure toys?

Yes. For people who want to add a jolt to their sex lives, vibrators can add a sense of playfulness, fun, and creativity. An already solid relationship can be enhanced with pleasure toys.

Why do some females use vibrators to orgasm? Is the reason that men can't satisfy them?

A 2005 study showed that about 25 percent of women orgasm from sexual intercourse.[11] This study also revealed that 70 percent of them need clitoral stimulation and more time to climax. Men might not feel threatened by vibrators when aware of these facts.

Do sex maniacs use vibrators?

No. Many men and women in the U.S. enjoy vibrators in sex play. They can't all be sex maniacs.

CHAPTER 2

Sex Toy Industry and Regulations

Over $20 billion is spent globally on adult pleasure toys, which are manufactured in several countries, including the U.S. Some of these toys cause injuries but aren't regulated by the U.S Food and Drug Administration (FDA). Pleasure toy sales are illegal in a few U.S. states.

Does the U.S. have safety regulations for pleasure toys?

The FDA classifies three types of vibrators as obstetrical and gynecological therapeutic medical devices: a powered vaginal muscle stimulator, a genital vibrator, and a clitoral engorgement device. These three devices are expensive and require a doctor's prescription. But, no government agencies inspect adult toys, and no legislation currently addresses the lack of regulations.

Moreover, though the Consumer Product Safety Commission (CPSC) oversees sales of pleasure toys, the CPSC doesn't require that these toys be tested for safety. Data is simply collected on dangerous products in reports from hospitals and coroners.

The CPSC also rules on children's toys that cause injuries equivalent to or less than those incurred from adult toys. For example, it has been reported that over an 11-year timespan, pleasure toys are responsible for 6,799 injuries, or 618 per year, whereas children's magnet toys are responsible for 1,700 injuries over a three-year period, or an average of 567 injuries per year.[12]

Which countries produce pleasure toys?

In 2020, China had 1000 factories nationwide manufacturing 70% of the global export of sex toys. Because of the pandemic and the resulting lockdown in several countries, China experienced a surge in orders for vibrators and sex dolls from France, Italy, and the U.S. One thousand sex dolls are exported each month from China.[13] Some companies manufacture products in the U.S., Sweden, Germany, and Great Britain.

Is the global market for pleasure toys growing?

Revenue for the sex toy industry was approximately $33.64 billion in 2020.[14] This industry is projected to experience an 8.04-percent revenue growth for the years spanning from 2021 to 2028.[15]

How much money do U.S. consumers spend on pleasure toys?

In 2020, the adult toy industry was estimated to be worth $9 billion. Adult sex stores derive 80 percent of their revenue from products provided by this industry. In addition, women spent about $5 billion on pleasure toys at home parties. Baby boomer women purchase 60 percent of their toys from adult sex shops. Couples are also driving increased sales of pleasure toys.[16,17] A recent development is the growing popularity of vibrators for couples.

Does the U.S. manufacture pleasure toys?

Doc Johnson manufactures about 75 percent of its adult pleasure toys in California.[18] The Los Angeles Magazine describes

Doc Johnson as "the Procter and Gamble of sex toys."[19] This company even sells pleasure toys on Amazon.com.

Bad Dragon Enterprises manufactures custom-made toys from platinum-cured silicone. The company's prolific inventory includes small and regular-size dildos, penetrable toys, dragon-realistic dildos, penis extensions, and packing. Transgender people (female to male) and those who cross-dress as males wear packing or padding in underwear to simulate a penis.

Bad Dragon Enterprises makes animal pleasure toys that have human traits and personalities. These toys wear clothing, speak, walk on two legs, and show emotion, intelligence, and facial expressions. The toys also appeal to members of the furry fandom, a subculture fascinated by erotic art and furry-themed cybersex. These members meet at furry conventions or on the Internet. Yiff, a slang term, is indicative of sex between animal characters and the fandom. Registered users on Bad Dragon's website can activate fantasy mode to view imaginative descriptions, photos, stories, and pictures.

Liberator Inc., also known as One-up Innovations, makes Liberator Shapes. The company's adult pillows enable baby boomers and those with disabilities to easily manage sexual positions.

OhMiBod produces remote-control vibrating pleasure toys for iPod and iPhone users. Noise from remote vibrators is heard over an iPod's earbuds.[20]

SquarePeg Toys makes large silicone toys for fetish anal play in a market dominated by vinyl.

In Southern California, Hankey's Toys manufactures dildos raging in size from extra small to giant.

Children of the Revolution (COTR) produces toys pleasurable for all bodies. COTR is owned by Alice Sinclair, a sex educator.

Minna was formed by engineers and product designers at Stanford to produce well-made vibrators.

Can people buy pleasure toys everywhere in the U.S.?

The Obscene Device law was passed in Texas in 1973 and updated in 2003 to forbid sales of adult toys. This law was never repealed. A U.S. district court judge states that this law is "facially unconstitutional and unenforceable."[21]

An Alabama law that bans sales but not possession of pleasure toys was passed in 1998. In 2007, the United States Supreme Court declined to hear a case on the ban. A legal loophole permits the sale of pleasure toys for "medical, scientific, educational, legislative, judicial, or law enforcement" grounds.[22]

Pleasure toy enthusiasts in Alabama must complete an anonymous form at brick-and-mortar sex shops. The form contains ten questions that must be answered to determine whether a customer or his or her partner experiences difficulty with sexual satisfaction. Alabama residents can avoid this procedure by traveling to nearby states to buy toys.

Adult shop owners in Alabama must be very careful about selling toys as medical devices. Penalties for doing so include up to one year in prison with a $10,000 fine for the first offense. A second offense increases jail time from one to ten years.[23]

Georgia and Mississippi have similar laws. Laws prohibiting the sale of pleasure toys were struck down in Louisiana, Kansas, and Colorado.[24,25]

CHAPTER 3

Pleasure Toys and Sexual Health

Pleasure toys enhance sexual health for adults. Women who are unable to orgasm during sexual intercourse can do so with vibrators. Men masturbate with them, and a prostate massager can improve the sexual health and sexual satisfaction of men.

The demand for pleasure toys has increased dramatically during the recent COVID-19 pandemic.

Why do people use pleasure toys?

Remember the passion you and your partner experienced when learning about each other's body at the beginning of your relationship? If your sex life has become boring, you can add excitement with pleasure toys. They're learning tools. They can be used to show your partner how to touch you in pleasurable ways.

It's best to demonstrate how a vibrator can enhance pleasure. After all, most people are visual learners. Ultimately, adult toys can make good sex even better. They can also be used to treat symptoms of several sexual disorders, including erectile dysfunction, genital arousal disorder, and hypoactive sexual desire disorder, which is characterized by the lack of sexual fantasies and desire for sex. Pleasure toys are the easiest or only way for 25 percent of sexually normal women to climax.

Antidepressants, antihistamines, and medications for cancer, blood pressure, and heart disease affect sexual function and satisfaction for women and men. That's why boomers can benefit from using pleasure toys.

Transgender people are likely to experience gender dysphoria (GD), a feeling of distress that a mismatch exists between their gender identity, or sense of being male or female, and the biological sex assigned to them at birth. Nonbinary is a term used by individuals who view sexual orientation and/or gender identity as fluid. Transgender and nonbinary people use pleasure toys to affirm their gender identity.

Do pleasure toys help people enjoy sexual activity?

A vibrator can provide older people with the stimulation necessary to climax. In general, men and women can benefit from the use of pleasure toys. Women can use these toys for genital lubrication. Men can use dildos during sex play to reduce the pressure to maintain an erection. Sexual partners plan the use of pleasure toys together. Doing so makes sex more exciting and creates greater sexual intimacy.

What unexpected benefits do women and men gain from using pleasure toys?

Pleasure toys are helpful for enhancing sexual activity, satisfaction, and orgasm, as well as for improving sleep, relieving pain, healing wounds faster, strengthening the immune system, increasing brain power, decreasing stress, and reducing menopausal sweating during the night.

Do pleasure toys promote women's sexual health?

Adult toy use is associated with behaviors that promote health and a positive sexuality.[26] Women who use vibrators are more likely to schedule gynecological exams and perform a self-exam.[27]

How often do women orgasm during penile to vaginal sex (PIV)?

Based on 33 studies in Elizabeth Lloyd's book, *The Case of the Female Orgasm*, only 25.3 percent of women consistently orgasm during intercourse. About 50 percent are sometimes orgasmic, 20 percent rarely have orgasms, and 5 percent never have orgasms.[28] Vibrators are the only way that many women can climax.

Can pleasure toys treat women's health conditions?

Adult toys are beneficial in treating menopausal and postmenopausal symptoms, as well as other health conditions.[29]

Female sexual dysfunctions, including anorgasmia, arousal, and desire disorders, are treated with vibrators.[30] Vaginal atrophy, pain in the vulva and vagina, and tightness result from vaginismus, vulvodynia, lichen sclerosis, gynae cancer treatments, and surgical procedures. Women who have multiple sclerosis experience less desire, reduced lubrication, and longer time to achieve orgasm with decreased pleasure.

How are these conditions defined?

Anorgasmia is the medical term used to describe regular difficulty having an orgasm after ample stimulation.

Vaginal atrophy occurs frequently after menopause. In this condition, the vaginal walls thin, dry, and become inflamed when the body has less estrogen, making intercourse painful.

Vaginismus is caused by a muscle spasm in the pelvic floor muscles. This condition makes it painful or impossible to have penile-vaginal intercourse (PIV).

Vulvodynia is chronic pain in the vulva, the area outside a woman's genitals. Among the symptoms are burning, stinging, and itching that can last more than three months. The cause is unknown.

Lichen sclerosis is patchy, white skin developing in the genital and anal areas. The skin appears thinner than normal. Post-menopausal women are at higher risk.

Gynae cancer treatments for gynecologic cancer are surgery, chemotherapy, and radiation. A gynecologic oncologist is trained to treat cancers in a woman's reproductive system.

Which specific pleasure toys treat vaginal atrophy and tightness and pain in the vulva and vagina?

Many women favor slim vaginal vibrators over clinical dilators often prescribed by physicians. Dilators stretch the tissue of the vagina without pain. Vibrations increase blood circulation in the vaginal walls. Lubrication is increased and nerves are stimulated. Local anesthetic gels, medication, and psychological treatments complement the use of vaginal vibrators.

Do pleasure toys promote men's sexual health?

Men's sexual problems include erectile dysfunction, premature ejaculation, lack of libido, and post-surgery concerns. Specific pleasure toys can help resolve these health conditions.

Constriction rings help men keep their erections firm, and specially-designed vibrators help men with delayed ejaculation. In addition, men experience various sexual sensations when using penile sleeves for manual masturbation. There are also some vibrators and penile suction devices that help men attain and keep an erection and stimulate nerve endings. These devices can be purchased with or without a prescription. It's helpful to get medical advice before using them.

Penile prostheses, usually referred to as strap-on harnesses, are typically used by women. The straps hold a dildo, a packer, or any pleasure toy against the body. Some harnesses may go around the thigh or can be worn as underwear or as jock straps.

A male who cannot get an erection may use penile prostheses to have penile-vaginal intercourse (PIV).

Can pleasure toys treat men's health conditions?

Cases of prostatitis, benign prostate hyperplasia (BPH), and prostate cancer can be reduced by massaging the prostate gland.[31] Prostatitis is a swelling of the prostate gland. BPH is a common health condition that men experience as part of the aging process.

In this condition, the prostate gland becomes enlarged, squeezing the urethra and limiting the flow of urine. A prostate massage helps reduce the risk of prostate cancer. The National Cancer Institute links regular ejaculation to a decreased risk for prostate cancer.[32,33]

Why is a prostate massage beneficial?

The prostatic duct connects the prostate gland to the urinary system, and semen is stored in the prostate gland. A prostate massage eliminates stagnant semen and bacterial growth in the duct and prevents swelling. It also improves circulation of seminal fluid and strengthens urine flow. A prostate massage ends painful ejaculations.[34]

Prostate massage therapy was the only treatment available before antibiotics. Some men choose a prostate massage, foregoing medical interventions. It's an effective procedure that relieves symptoms of an enlarged prostate. A prostate orgasm is a wonderful side benefit from a prostate massage. This type of orgasm is intense, pleasurable, and lengthy.[35]

How should one prepare for a manual prostate massage?

Use warm water and soap to wash the external and internal areas of the anus. Insert a disposable bulb enema into the anus using warm water. Apply a good amount of lube before insertion. The anus is ready when water runs clear. Givers in anal sex should wash their hands for 20 seconds. Cut and trim the fingernails. Then clean the fingernails with a nail brush. Exert pressure on the perineum, the skin between the scrotum and the anus. Men who want more sensation use a prostate massager.

What is the preparation for a prostate massage with an anal toy?

Use antibacterial soap to clean an anal toy. Cover the massager with a condom to be safe.[36] Wash the anal passageway, following the instructions above to ensure cleanliness. Take a bath to relax. Apply additional lubricant on the anus and prostate massager. A water-based lube is compatible with prostate massagers made of silicone, TPR, TPE, or Cyberskin.

How is a prostate massager inserted into the anus?

It's not uncomfortable if done correctly. Stimulate the anus and perineum before inserting the massager. Aim the curved tip of the toy at the naval area, slowly insert the toy into the anus, and move the toy gently to find the prostate (P-spot). Despite differences in height and weight, 98 percent of the prostate gland is two to three inches inside the anus.

Which positions are comfortable for insertion of a prostate massager?

Three positions are suggested for solo sex:

Lie on your back and bend and pull your legs to your chest. Place a small pad under your lower back.

Lie on your side and bend and pull one of your legs to your chest.

Crouch down and squat over the massager.

Assume the knee-elbow position with a partner.[37]

What does a prostate orgasm feel like?

A prostate massage leads to an orgasm without ejaculation. If excited during the massage, the man can masturbate and a strong orgasm can happen, but it won't be a prostate orgasm.[38] The "male P-spot" provides orgasms three to ten times stronger than penile orgasms.[39]

Covid-19

Can pleasure toys transmit the coronavirus?

Clean pleasure toys thoroughly if sharing them within a 72-hour period. Wash your hands for 20 seconds.

The new coronavirus (SARS-Cov-2) remains active on some surfaces for three days,[40] although some recent studies refute this statement. Don't use hand sanitizers on toys because the sanitizers can irritate the vagina or rectum.

Is it safe to buy new pleasure toys during the pandemic?

It may be safer to buy pleasure toys online than at adult brick-and-mortar stores. In e-commerce transactions, no one physically touches credit cards or cash, and pleasure toys are usually packaged in cardboard. The coronavirus can live on these toys for 24 hours, surviving up to three days on plastic and steel.[41,42]

Recent research indicates that the coronavirus degrades on surfaces in a few hours. But, despite this new fact, it's wise to be careful. Open the box or wait 24 hours. And, make sure you wash your hands for 20 seconds. Lab studies of the coronavirus on surfaces may not be relevant in your home.[43]

In large warehouses, employees might not follow social distancing guidelines or might work while ill if sick pay isn't available.[44] Websites might not be the best place to buy toys during a pandemic. A safe option is to buy adult pleasure toys at Target, CVS, Walmart, or at a small sex shop.

Should pleasure toys be shared with a partner who also has COVID-19?

Have solo sex. Sex partners who test positive for COVID-19 shouldn't assume they've acquired immunity until 14 days have passed. Scientists also don't know enough about reinfection. People may be infected but haven't been tested.[45]

Can my partner who has COVID-19 still have sex?

Don't have sex with your partner if he or she is infected with COVID-19, even if asymptomatic. The World Health Organization (WHO) indicates that the risk of household transmission ranges from three to ten percent.[46]

CHAPTER 4

Overview of Pleasure Toys

Shopping for vibrators, dildos, anal toys, prostate massagers, and blow-up dolls is a fun and eye-opening experience, and it's certainly possible to find the best pleasure toys for first-time users and baby boomers. A variety of these toys are available for solo or partner sex.

Farley Malorrus, owner of Bosko's Oso blow-up dolls, imported Judy, an inflatable doll, from Japan. She was 5 feet 2 inches tall with a perfect figure made of vinyl. Malorrus strapped an artificial vagina on Judy and doubled the price for a loving companion. To ensure that the doll was sturdy, Malorrus asked a friend who lived on the 20th floor in a high-rise building to test Judy.

The friend got drunk and banged Judy every night. One night, he was interrupted during sex by a loud pop followed by a hissing sound. Judy slowly deflated. The friend was so angry and drunk that he punched Judy and threw her out the window into heavy traffic. Drivers skidded to avoid Judy, who they believed was a real person.[47]

How did interest in buying vibrators begin?

In August 1998, "The Turtle and the Hare" episode of *Sex and the City* featured the rabbit vibrator, which then became a pop culture success, ushering in the beginning of sexual consumerism. Females then entered adult sex shops to buy the rabbit vibrator they saw on *Sex and the City*.[48]

Where can vibrators be purchased?

You can buy pleasure toys in adult sex stores and on the Internet. They're also available at CVS, Walgreens, Safeway, Kroger, Target, Walmart, the Wirecutter Division of the New York Times, MOMA's Design Store, and the Museum of Sex in NYC.

A Google search for vibrators yields 23,000,000 results. Adam and Eve, a national online sex toy shop, offers 524 different types of vibrators. And, Amazon.com has 400 website pages listing pleasure toy products.

Are there brick-and-mortar sex shops that shouldn't be visited?

Avoid sex shops near strip clubs and with names such as XXX-World.[49] Many of these shops are disrespectful to women. Consumers are unable to touch or smell pleasure toys there to determine whether they contain chemicals because the toys are packaged.

Do brick-and-mortar sex stores target feminists and the LGBTQIAP+ community?

Shops geared towards feminists and the LGBTQIAP+ community sell a variety of pleasure toys for people of all gender identities and sexual orientations. Salespeople at these stores are knowledgeable and provide a comfortable environment for women and men. You can view Appendix A for a list of sex shops serving feminists, couples, and the LGBTQIAP+ community.

Should you buy pleasure toys on Amazon.com and eBay?

Chinese companies sell pleasure toys on Amazon.com that may be toxic. Sex swings and sex furniture are less expensive and safe to buy there. New and used pleasure toys are sold on eBay and might not be body safe.

Vibrators

All vibrators have motors producing enjoyable sensations throughout the body. The vibrating head and handle stimulate the genitalia and anus. Genital discomfort from vibrators is rare.

Which power sources are available for vibrators?

The power sources include rechargeable batteries, disposable batteries, and wall current. Avoid using less powerful rechargeable batteries that have a lower voltage of 1.2 V.

Alkaline or disposable batteries are much stronger with a voltage of 1.5 V. Some toy manufacturers advise users not to purchase rechargeable batteries.

How are vibrators used?

Women use vibrators to stimulate the vagina, vulva, and clitoris when masturbating and during sexual intercourse and oral sex. Men use vibrators to stimulate the penis, scrotum, perineum, prostate, or anus. Some vibrators have a remote control and can be used underwater.

Which sizes, shapes, speeds, and noise levels of vibrators are available?

Vibrators are available in all sizes, shapes, designs, colors, and textures. Most vibrators used in vaginal or anal penetration are equivalent to the size of an average erect penis, 5.2 inches long with a 4.6-inch circumference. Shapes of vibrators vary from narrow bullets, animals, ergonomic forms, and miniature rockets to huge human tongues.

Modern vibrators have settings for speed, intensity, pulsation, and noise. The vibration speed of multi-speed vibrators is adjustable, enabling you to press a button to increase or lower the speed. Check the vibrator for the intensity of sensations and noise. Quieter vibrators are made from soft material.

What does a smart vibrator do?

You can control a remote vibrator with Bluetooth from an app on a smartphone, but the partner with the remote shouldn't be too far away.

Some pleasure toys can be controlled from anywhere on Earth, and long-distance relationships can thrive when the partner controls the vibrations. During the COVID-19 pandemic, remote toys have become useful for partners living apart from each other.

A remote-controlled toy can also be placed in panties. Several toys are even quiet enough to be worn in public, and some of them have a timer to wake a woman up with gentle vibrations, which can be controlled by a partner.

A Waterproof Smart Phone APP Bluetooth Remote Vibration Massager Stick costs about $37.98.

Which types of vibrators are available?

Among the vibrators described in the *Beginners Guide to Vibrators* are external vibrators, internal vibrators, wand massagers, clitoral vibrators, tongue vibrators, G-spot vibrators, bullet vibrators, egg vibrators, mini vibrators, finger vibrators, wand-shaped medium-sized vibrators, butterfly vibrators, self-propelled vibrators, dual-type vibrators, and partner vibrators.[50]

External vibrators can stimulate the clitoris, enhancing sexual pleasure and orgasms.

Internal vibrators are inserted in the vagina, targeting the G-spot. They're similar to dildos.

Wand massagers knead muscles in the body and work wonders stimulating the vulva. Attachments stimulate the vagina, clitoris, and the G-spot.

Clitoral vibrators deliver air or vibrations to the clitoris. Women experience fantastic orgasms with these vibrators.

Tongue vibrators are terrific for oral sex.

G-spot vibrators are curved. Stimulation of the G-spot leads to sexual arousal, strong orgasms, and possibly female ejaculation.

A small extension on the rabbit vibrator's shaft stimulates the clitoris.

Bullet and egg vibrators are small and portable.

A mini vibrator can fit in your hand and can be used to stimulate the clitoris and prostate gland. This small toy is also useful for sex in a dark place. Some mini vibrators can even imitate oral sex.

Finger vibrators fasten to your finger. Either partner can wear it and provide intense stimulation.

Wand-shaped medium-sized vibrators are effective for big women or those with limited hand strength who have difficulty reaching the vagina and G-spot.

Butterfly vibrators can be held over the vagina with straps and provide hand-free masturbation and foreplay.

Realistic vibrators have ridges, veins, and bumps.

Vibrators that rotate and thrust can deliver self-propelled penetration.

Some vibrators with advanced materials warm up immediately to match the heat of the user's body.

Dual-type vibrators stimulate the clitoris, G-spot, and anus simultaneously during masturbation and partner sex.

A man's prostate gland (P-spot) can be stimulated with anal vibrators in solo and partner sex. Sometimes, the narrow shaft of these vibrators has a beaded or ridged surface.

Partner vibrators are multi-purpose. The gentle curves and stimulating surfaces arouse the clitoris, anus, and the penis.

You can stimulate vulva-vaginal tissue by covering the clitoris and labia with a large vibrator. You can also combine a dildo with vibrators during sex.

How are waterproof vibrators used in sex play?

Waterproof vibrators are fun in the shower, bathtub, and swimming pool.

What indicates that a vibrator is waterproof?

A waterproof vibrator will contain an O-ring, which creates a watertight seal and is found around the edge in the battery compartment. Always make sure that the battery compartment is tight to prevent water from leaking inside. The battery cover might loosen if the toy has a twist dial base for changing the speed from gentle to strong.

Can you recommend a vibrator for a beginner?

The first vibrator that you use should improve circulation in the clitoris and labia. The body needs time to adjust to sensations from a vibrator.[51]

What is the best vibrator to use after menopause?

Blood circulation in the clitoris is slower in baby boomer women. A stronger powered vibrator increases lubrication and results in potent orgasms. Dr. Barb DePree tells patients to use vibrators to keep sex alive and learn about their body.[52] Power the vibrator using an electric wall outlet because it takes longer to achieve an orgasm after menopause.

How should I begin using a new vibrator?

Wash the vibrator before using it the first time and then charge it. It's best to apply a lot of lubricant to the vibrator and to figure out which speed is pleasurable during masturbation. Don't stimulate the clitoris directly for too long because it can become irritated. Instead, use indirect stimulation. Using a vibrator leads to many exquisite orgasms.

Dildos

Dildos have been around for 28,000 years. A stone penis-shaped dildo was discovered along a German mountain range in 2005.[53]

How many people purchase dildos in the United States?

Lovehoney, a sex toy company, surveyed 11,400 adults in 2018 and found that three out of every four people own at least one dildo.[54] Women buy more dildos than men.[55] Lovehoney attributes 12 percent of its global sales of dildos to the United States.

People over 30 are more likely to purchase dildos than millennials, who range from 18 to 30 years old.[56,57] Iowa purchases the most dildos, and the South buys the fewest.[58,59] The Midwest and some states on the East and West coasts are interested in playing with this pleasure toy.[60]

How are dildos shaped and used?

Most dildos used in vaginal or anal penetration are equivalent to the size of an average erect penis, which is 5.2 inches long with a 4.6-inch girth. The size of Lovehoney's Lifelike Lover dildo ranges from 5.5 inches to 10 inches.[61] In Lovehoney's survey, 5 percent of the respondents have used a 12-inch dildo.[62]

View Appendix B for sex toy companies that sell extra small and giant-size dildos.

Do women or men prefer dildos?

Men climax almost twice as much as women do with a dildo.[63] Most women don't insert dildos into their vagina. The tip or shaft indirectly touches the clitoris. Many women need a vibrator to experience an orgasm.

How should I choose a dildo?

First, determine which size you need. A small dildo may be ineffective for arousal, and a bigger one might be uncomfortable. Most dildos are made of five types of material: jelly or elastomer, silicone, soft skin, acrylic, or glass.

Silicone is the only nonporous material that can be hard or soft. Dual-density silicone dildos are soft on the outside with a hard-inside core.[64] In 2020, Phallophile Reviews rated the most realistic dildos and the self-thrusting dildo.[65]

Anal Pleasure Toys

Anal toys are used for external and internal stimulation. Anal vibrators are smaller than those used in the vagina.

Who buys prostate massagers?

New York City accounts for 27 percent of sales of prostate massagers. Men over 50 in Miami buy the most. Men and women purchase 70 percent of massagers in Las Vegas. Men in San Francisco are seven times more likely to own an anal toy than men in Los Angeles. Women account for 66 percent of sales in Salt Lake City. Men in Chicago are the primary purchasers of prostate massagers.[66]

In the United Kingdom, there are more purchases of prostate massagers than in the United States. Anal pleasure toys are equally popular in Russia and the U.S. Women in Spain buy more prostate massagers than men. This may indicate that heterosexual partners are interested in anal toys.

Older Italian men are more likely to purchase anal pleasure toys than older French men. However, younger people in France are more interested in anal toys than the older generation.[67]

What are anal vibrators?

Most are butt plugs or phallus-like vibrators. The sizes vary from 4 to 6 inches in length with a 1-inch width. Anal vibrators are available in various shapes. A long handle with a flared shape prevents the toy from falling inside the rectum. Apply a good amount of lubricant when using an anal pleasure toy. Insert an anal vibrator carefully to prevent the rectal lining from tearing.

Butt Plugs

These anal toys are the size of a finger and are good for beginners. The butt plug stays inside the anus and can be powered by batteries or can be linked by wire to a power pack. Vibrating butt plugs are used in solo or partner sex. You will experience fullness and vibrations in the rectum when using this type of pleasure toy.

Anal Beads

Fifty Shades of Grey, the book trilogy, sparked interest in anal beads. Users of anal beads derive pleasure from inserting the beads into the anus and removing them. Small beads or balls vibrate at various speeds and link through a long cord to a power device. Individual beads can be different sizes.

Beginners typically start off with smaller anal beads and move on to larger beads when ready. All anal beads have a ring at the end to make it easier to pull them out during solo sex, preventing slippage into the anal cavity.

It's a good idea to buy easy-to-clean plastic or silicone anal beads or balls. Anal beads connected by nylon strings are difficult to clean.

Blow-up Dolls

Blow-up dolls look realistic and can be either female or male. Each one can be used as a substitute for a sex partner. A whole-body blow-up female doll will have a vagina, mouth, and limbs. Some dolls have only a torso. Male dolls have attachments, including an erect penis and a flaccid penis.[68]

Some interesting facts about blow-up dolls.

Davecat, a man in Michigan, says his blow-up doll is his wife, although not legally wed. He owns two other pleasure dolls, each of which has a Twitter account.

In Japan, sex dolls were often called Dutch wives. Dutch sailors who were on a ship for months made dolls out of leather and traded them to Japanese men.

The Barbie doll was created in the 1950s, and the source of inspiration for the doll was the Bild Lilli, an erotic German sex doll with no openings.

iDollators are people who are into blow-up dolls. Davecat states that "98 percent of iDollators treat their pleasure dolls like goddesses." Some men view them as companions, claiming that relationships with real women are too difficult. Dolls don't possess unpleasant human qualities.[69]

The popularity of the modern sex doll is attributed to Howard Stern. He had sex with a RealDoll on air and then orders for the doll rose. In 2014, the RealDoll company sold about 300 dolls per year, costing a maximum of $5000 for each.[70]

Are blow-up dolls expensive?

Silicone dolls are soft to the touch, making them more realistic and expensive. Pleasure dolls are priced differently. They cost between $2000 and $10,000.[71] A realistic doll can cost less than $500. But, for a fantastic doll, be prepared to spend $3000. Some dolls are available for less than $100. Shop around, read reviews, and listen to other owners of blow-up dolls.

What is the material of a blow-up doll?

Initially, the outer material of dolls was made of solid latex but was later switched to silicone.

In June 2009, Abyss Creations, a doll company, changed the doll material from tin cure silicone to platinum silicone. Current blow-up dolls are less likely to tear and don't have the compression marks seen in earlier prototypes.

SiliconeWives produces pleasure dolls from TPE (thermoplastic rubber) material and premium silicone. These dolls have a durable interior and use a metal skeleton with flexible joints. Owners of these dolls can screw them in different sexual positions.[72]

Are dolls made to suit a variety of tastes?

SiliconeWives' blow-up doll catalogue enables shoppers to customize the dolls by choosing the lip color, skin complexion, eye color, fingernail and toenail color, makeup, hair color, pubic hair, nipples, and vaginal insertion method of the dolls. Also available are mini dolls and pleasure doll torsos.

In 2003, Abyss Creations created the Face-X system, which made it possible to use interchangeable faces on blow-up dolls. In 2011, this company produced nine female bodies and 16 female faces that were available to owners of sex dolls.

In 2009, RealDoll designed removable inserts for the mouth, vagina, and face that could be attached to sex dolls with magnets instead of Velcro. This company offered 31 faces and 11 female body types as of 2015.[73]

Do women buy male pleasure dolls?

Synthetic dolls weigh between 75 and 115 pounds. Weight is one reason that not many women purchase pleasure dolls.[74] Another reason is that blow-up dolls can't perform cunnilingus. Females who own male sex dolls account for 10 percent of RealDoll's sales. Some women buy female dolls.[75]

Choices for male dolls are limited, but female dolls are customizable. The first male RealDoll, Charlie, was withdrawn from production in 2008. Two body types and three head types replaced Charlie.

Are transgender dolls available for sale?

Yes. RealDoll sells them, but they must be customized.

CHAPTER 5

Pleasure Toys for Baby Boomers

Sexual activity can be enhanced with pleasure toys for solo or partner sex. People who have difficulty reaching climax can orgasm with a toy, and orgasms provide physical and psychological health benefits.

In this chapter, suggested pleasure toys for women and men are described and illustrated with approximate prices, which range from inexpensive to costly. Prices may increase or decrease depending on the place of purchase.

Which health benefits do women and men receive from having an orgasm during solo or partner sex with a toy?

During an orgasm, the human body releases natural chemicals such as endorphins, dopamine, and serotonin into the bloodstream. The benefits of an orgasm include intense pleasure, lowered blood pressure, faster wound healing, and improved sleep patterns. In addition, during an orgasm, pain thresholds rise, blocking pain and curing migraines. The cardiovascular system is also strengthened by the human orgasm, which can help tone the body.

Self-pleasure with a toy will increase your sexual knowledge. That's why you should explore how sensations and movements affect your sense of sexual satisfaction. Find out what turns you on. You can experience orgasms in different ways by using a pleasure toy to apply different types of stimulation to your genitals.

Women who masturbate are better able to orgasm with their partners, and orgasms are stronger when the pelvic muscles have been strengthened through the use of pleasure toys.

Self-pleasure with a toy can help reduce premature orgasms by teaching men to recognize the body's signals when ready to climax. It's possible for men to delay an orgasm by changing the stimulation, intensity, and speed of the pleasure toy.

There are also psychological benefits associated with having an orgasm. An individual's emotional health is connected to his or her ability to achieve an orgasm. Eastern sexologists believe the orgasm is a complete body experience. This wasn't the belief of Western sexologists, until recently.[76]

Why should baby boomer women use pleasure toys?

As women age, blood flow to the genitals is reduced. Postmenopausal women often experience vaginal dryness and lower libido. It takes longer for them to get aroused and to reach orgasm. Women who are unable to orgasm during sexual intercourse or oral intercourse can reach climax with pleasure toys.

Some women have aches, pains, and arthritis in their hands, wrists, and other joints. Masturbation can be very tiring. Pleasure toys make it easier to masturbate and to experience an orgasm. Adult toys stimulate the clitoris, vulva, G-spot, nipples, perineum, and anus.

Which pleasure toys work best for baby boomer women?

Pleasure toys made from silicone feel better on the body because the vaginal area becomes more sensitive as women age. The toy's strength is also important. Pleasure toys can satisfy individual tastes.

Pleasure Chest, an adult sex shop located in the West Village and Upper East Side in New York City, recommends the following toys for baby boomer women.[77]

Fiera Arouser for Her

The Fiera Arouser for Her is a small hands-free pleasure toy used to stimulate postmenopausal women. Its gentle suction action increases blood flow and lubrication. This pleasure toy prepares baby boomer women for sexual activity with partners. It costs about $199.

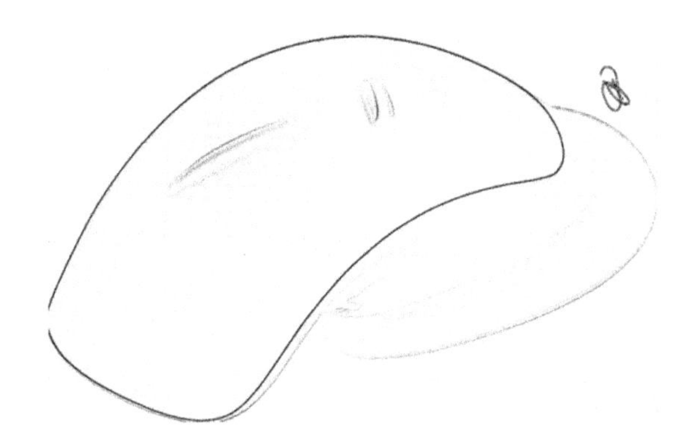

Fiera Arouser for Her

Magic Wand Original

This vibrator has been available since 1968. This pleasurable device has a dual purpose. It functions as a massager to relieve tense and sore muscles and as a vibrator to stimulate the genitals.

The Magic Wand Original is 12 inches long and has a cord connecting to a wall socket. The golf-ball shaped silicone head is 2.5 inches. This vibrator is so strong that it's recommended to women who are trying to have their first orgasm. The Magic Wand Original shuts off after 20 minutes of continuous use. Instructions indicate that it shouldn't be restarted, although users claim it can be turned on right away.[78]

The Magic Wand Original, formerly known as the Hitachi Magic Wand, is considered the "Cadillac" of all vibrators and is well known as the best vibrator for women to have an orgasm.[79,80]

During the 1970s, Betty Dodson taught women in body sex workshops how to use the Hitachi Magic Wand to have an orgasm. She suggested that women use a small towel to cover the genitals to reduce vibrations. This was known as the Betty Dodson Method.

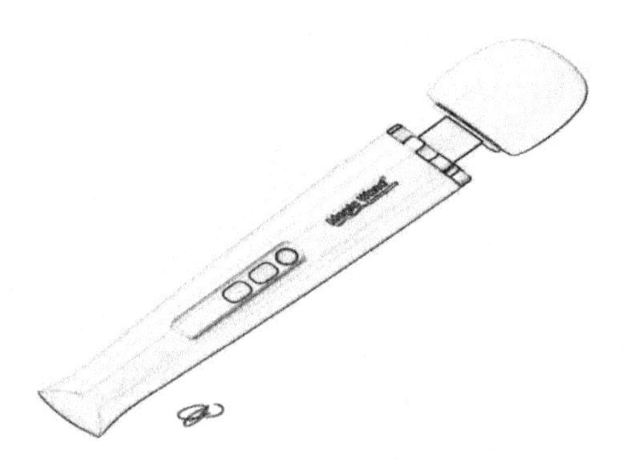

Magic Wand Original

After a 2002 episode of *Sex and the City* that featured the Hitachi Magic Wand, demand for this vibrator was so great that all units of the product were sold. Embarrassed by having its name linked to a sex toy, Hitachi planned to stop producing it in 2013. Persuaded to continue making this pleasure toy,

Hitachi changed the name of the toy to Magic Wand Original in 2013. Components, circuitry, and vibrating heads were improved in 2015. This rechargeable pleasure toy costs approximately $124.95. The G-spot and the P-spot Wand attachments fit this pleasure toy. Prices range from $20 to $30.

The PalmPower Massager

This small rechargeable massager is a best seller in Europe. Although weighing only seven ounces, it is powerful and competes with the Magic Wand Original.

The PalmPower has a solid handle, and the interchangeable cap is made of silicone. This massager comes with a cord and plug and costs about $59.95.

PalmPower Massager

LELO Smart Wand

This rechargeable waterproof pleasure toy made of ABS plastic can be used in the shower. Be careful not to slip and fall. Falls among older adults are the leading cause of fatal and nonfatal injuries.[81] The LELO Smart Wand costs about $199.

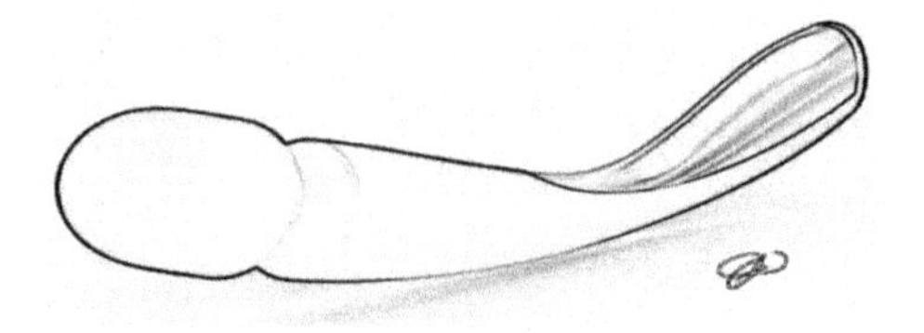

LELO Smart Wand

Rose Kegel Exercise Vaginal Weights

Use this exercise program for 15 minutes a day to strengthen vaginal muscles, maintain the vaginal wall's elasticity, and for bladder control. This leads to sexual satisfaction and stronger orgasms.

The six progressive weights are used in the Academy of Pelvic Health training courses This exercise program, made of medical-grade silicone, is recommended by doctors and sex therapists. The set costs about $49.99.

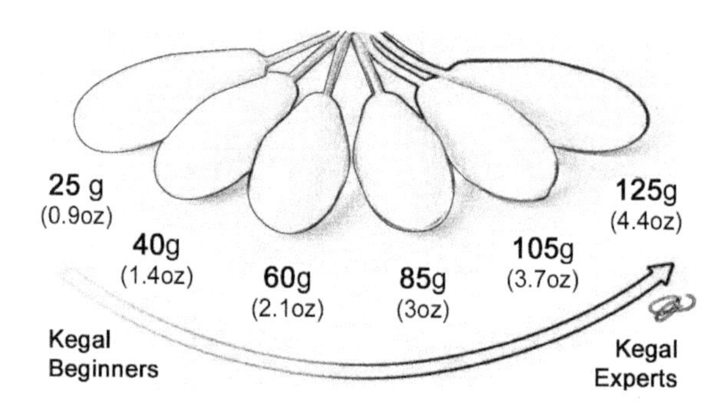

Rose Kegel Exercise Vaginal Weights

Eroscillator

This Swiss engineered pleasure toy was invented in 1996. The Eroscillator is an electrically operated and almost noiseless sexual stimulator. It's 7.5 inches long, weighs 8 ounces, has three speeds, and uses a 12-foot power cord for a 110-volt outlet. An oscillating engine and attachments are anchored to the motor, which is the only vibrating part.

Dr. Ruth Westheimer endorsed the Eroscillator based on an unpublished university study reporting more effectiveness than ordinary vibrators. This pleasure toy provides many more powerful and longer lasting orgasms.[82] Eroscillator 2 Golden Spoon attachments, designed for male and female erogenous zones, are covered with medical-grade silicone.

Use only water-based lubricants with this pleasure toy. Eroscillator Gold is expensive, costing from $109 to $469.95 depending on the model. It lasts ten years.[83]

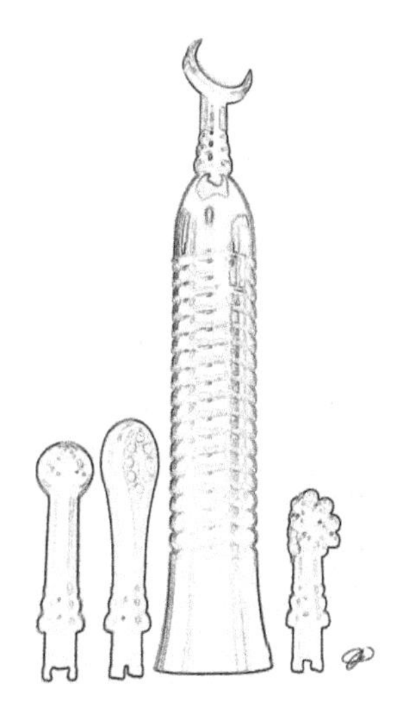

Eroscillator

Eva 2

This luxury waterproof vibrator is a good choice for baby boomer women because it's soft and hands-free. The Eva 2 is made of medical-grade silicone. It has one motor and three speeds, and the flexible wings from the product fold in beneath the labia for a snug fit. The Eva 2 provides clitoral stimulation during penile-vaginal intercourse. Dame Products sells the Eva 2 for approximately $135.

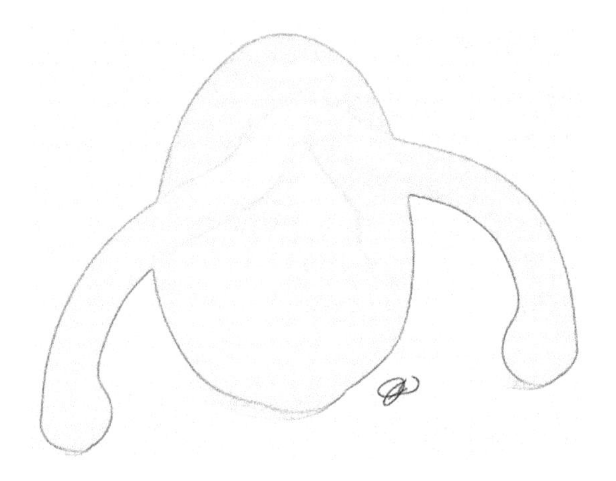

Eva 2

Oasis Vibrating Dilators

Women with vaginal atrophy or scarring, cancer, and vaginal pain or who had radiation treatment, surgery, or a sex change to female can benefit from vaginal renewal dilators that moisturize and massage the vagina. Follow a doctor's instructions or a sex therapist's instructions when using these dilators.

Apply lubricant or moisturizer to the dilator and insert the device to stretch the vagina.[84] The Oasis Vibrating Dilator set includes three narrow dilators in different thicknesses, a vibrating dilator, and one silicone-blend sleeve. Graduate to the next size when you are comfortable with the first dilator. The set is made of medical-grade ABS. Two AA batteries are not included in the price. The set costs about $46.00.

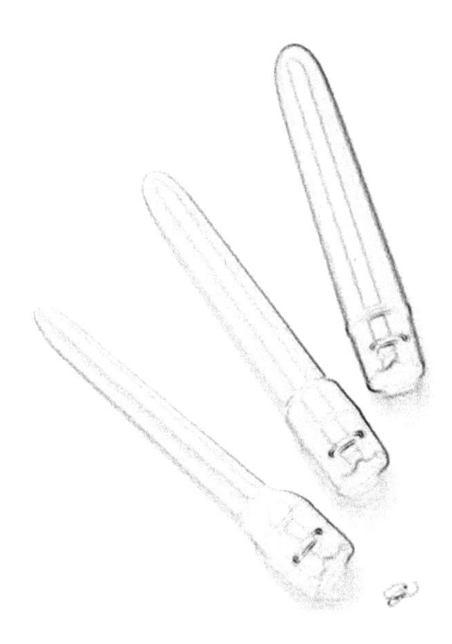

Oasis Vibrating Dilators

Why should baby boomer men use pleasure toys?

As men age, their testosterone levels decrease and their instances of erectile dysfunction (ED) increase. Pleasure toys can help men achieve and maintain an erection. Baby boomers who have aches and pains in their hands or wrists can masturbate with pleasure toys. A prostate massage (P-spot) is effective for promoting prostate health in aging men, and prostate orgasms are much stronger than penile orgasms.

Je Joue Mio Vibrating Ring

This elastic vibrating penis ring is made from silicone and constricts blood flow, helping men maintain an erection for longer periods of time. Use this pleasure toy during solo sex. You can also turn it around to vibrate the perineum, a very sensitive area. The Mio can be used to vibrate the woman's vulva during sexual activity with a partner. The price starts at $119.00.

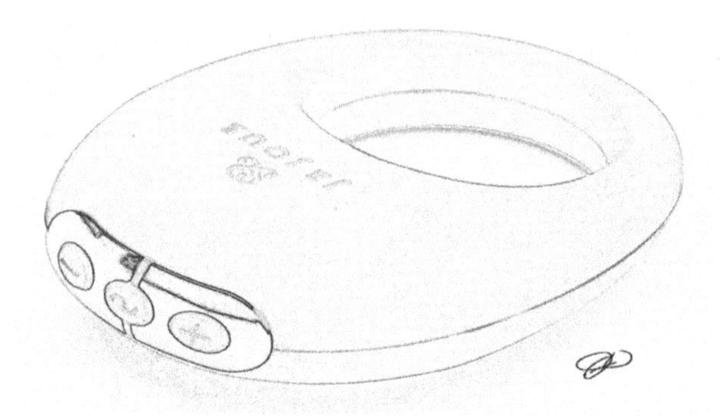

Je Joue Mio Vibrating Ring

Pulse Solo or Pulse Duo

This powerful pleasure toy and the remote control are made from silicone and ABS plastic (acrylonitrile butadiene styrene). The Pulse Solo has flexible wings that wrap around the penis. The Pulse stimulates the sensitive frenulum, an elastic band of tissue where the foreskin meets the underside of the penis. This pleasure toy helps men get hard in solo sex. Whether flaccid or erect, men will have an outstanding orgasm when using this toy. The Pulse Solo costs about $99. The Pulse Duo is meant for use in partner sex and can be purchased for approximately $199.

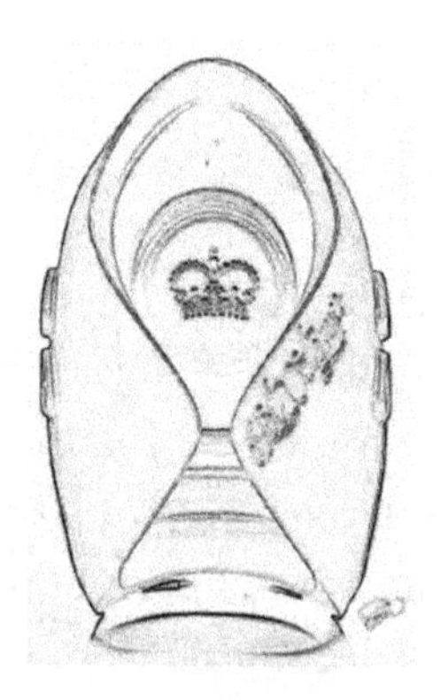

Pulse Solo

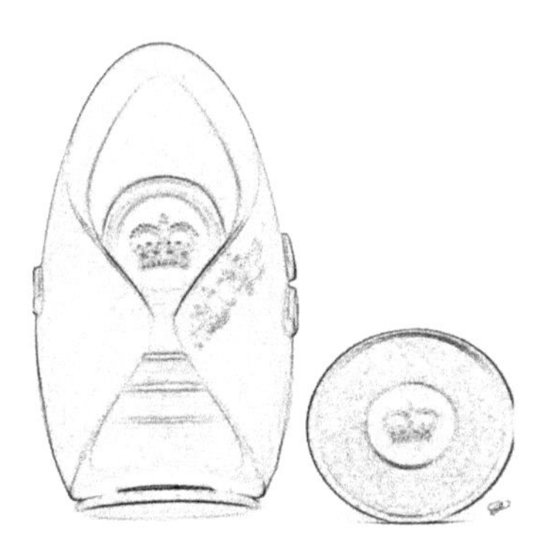

Pulse Duo

Fleshlight Flight Pilot

This light and easy-to-use masturbation sleeve is realistic, non-toxic, and porous. But, it's advertised on the company's website as body safe. The Fleshlight Flight Pilot can also be used with a partner when unable to have sexual intercourse. A masturbation sleeve works fine for men with average size penises. This pleasure toy is 6.9 inches long. The soft material inside bends to accommodate most men's penises.

Sensations are provided by adjustable suction, warmth, material, and textures inside the sleeve of the Fleshlight Flight Pilot. Four textures close to the sleeve's entrance are accessible. Its narrow width makes sensations feel more intense and leads to orgasms. The Fleshlight Flight Pilot comes with a small case and is portable. The price starts at about $49.95.

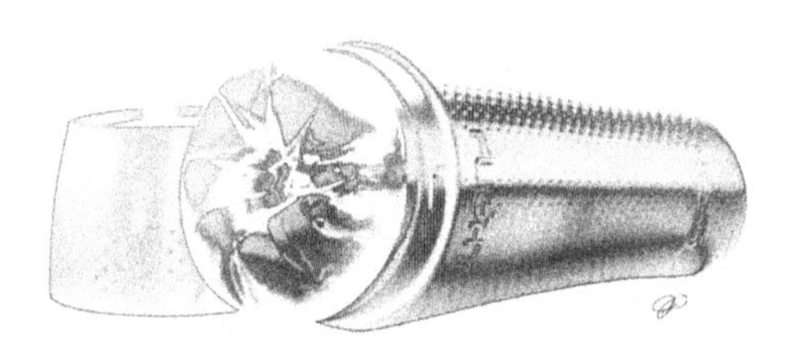

Fleshlight Flight Pilot

Simple Pleasure Prostate Massager

This pleasure massager contains 10 vibration modes that stimulate the prostate gland and enhance enjoyment. Slightly curved hands at its end prevent the massager from sliding in too far. Have fun in the shower with this waterproof device. Take care not to slip and fall.

The Simple Pleasure Prostate Massager is made from silicone and costs about $29.99.

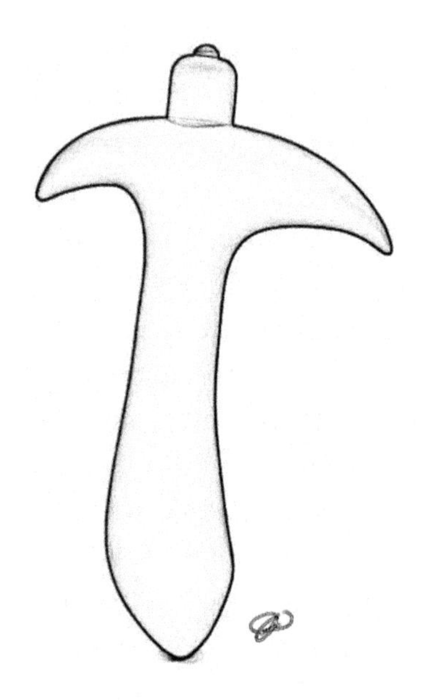

Simple Pleasure Prostate Massager

HUGO™

This waterproof prostate massager has two motors in its base and tip. The user time is two hours, and the massager is rechargeable. The HUGO™ is hands-free, has a remote control, and can be used for solo or partner sex. Produced by LELO, it's made of silicone/ABS plastic and costs about $186.15.

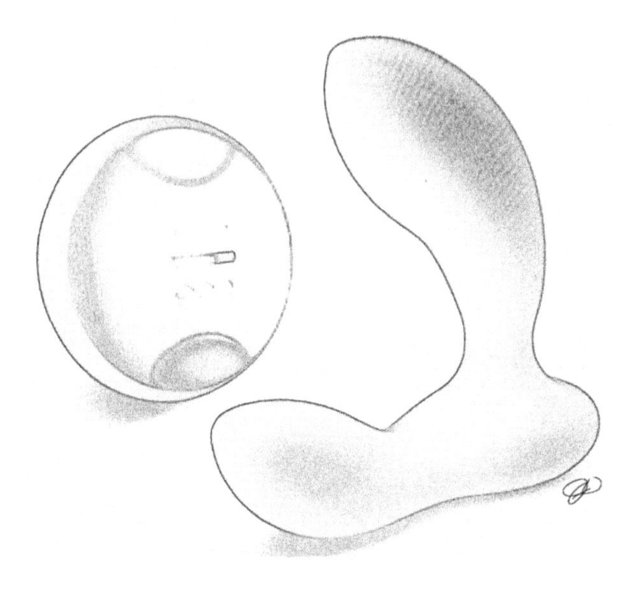

HUGO™

Palqueth 3

This curved P-spot (prostate gland) vibrator is hypoallergenic and is made of medical-grade silicone. The four-inch round top of the vibrator can be inserted into the rectum. This wireless anal toy operates remotely and has two intense motors, as well as eight vibration modes that stimulate the anal canal, P-spot, testicles, and perineum.

The Palqueth 3 increases blood flow to the prostate, improving circulation. This pleasure toy can also be used for solo and partner sex and is helpful for several types of sexual dysfunction, including ED and ejaculatory problems. The Palqueth 3 costs about $28.95.

For centuries, Asian cultures have promoted the massaging of the prostate gland. This massage technique provides health benefits and intense sexual pleasure. Health professionals in the West now recommend prostate massages.[85]

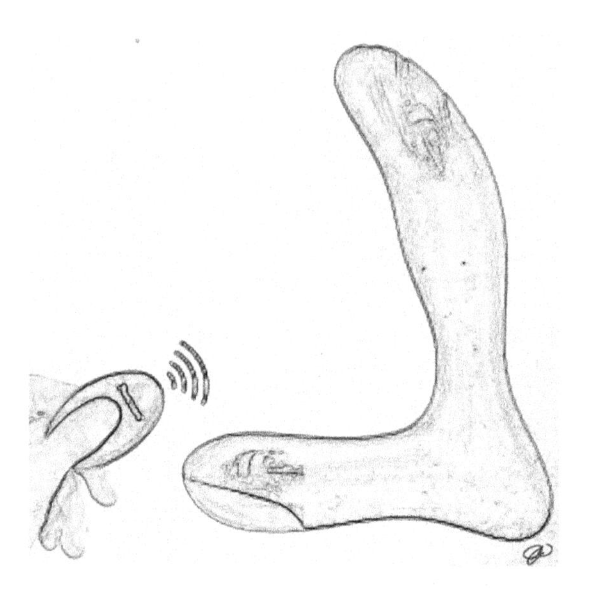

Palqueth 3

Pleasure Toys for Partners

Pleasure toys previously mentioned include the Magic Wand Original, the Eroscillator Golden Spoon attachments, Pulse Duo, the Rabbit vibrator, and Eva 2. They can also be used in partner sex.

Mystery Vibe Crescendo

The Crescendo is a soft, waterproof vibrator that weighs 5.6 ounces and is made from premium body-safe silicone. The vibrator is easy to hold and was designed to be unisex and gender neutral. This pleasure toy is capable of stimulating the clitoris and G-spot simultaneously.

The Crescendo bends in six different places to form any shape such as a J shape that curves around the head of the penis. Be careful, though. The Crescendo doesn't have a flared base that would prevent it from falling into the rectum during anal sex play.

This sex toy has six powerful and quiet motors providing 12 vibration modes and 16 pre-set speeds. The motors are located along the shaft and can be programmed by the user. Download the MysteryVibe app from Apple's App Store or Google Play. Place the Crescendo on the Qi wireless charging system pad with rechargeable batteries. The charge lasts an hour. The Mystery Vibe Crescendo costs about $179.

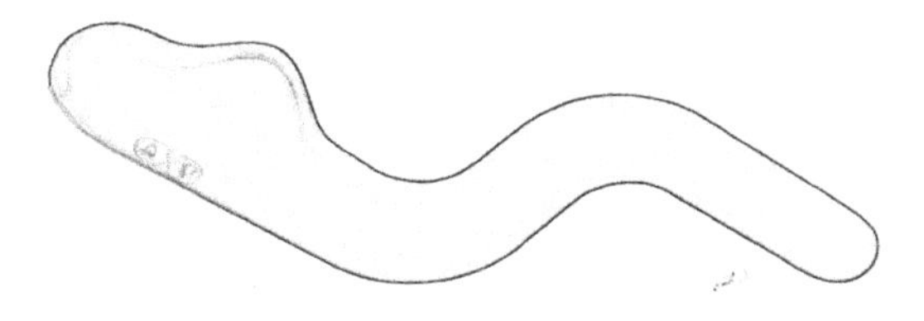

Mystery Vibe Crescendo

Melt by We-Vibe

This slim pleasure toy is made from body-safe silicone and fits between two partners in any position. The toy is comfortable to hold and provides light suction and pulsating waves of air to massage the clitoris. The We-Connect app allows your partner to control stimulation while the Melt is held in the right spot. The price starts at about $149.

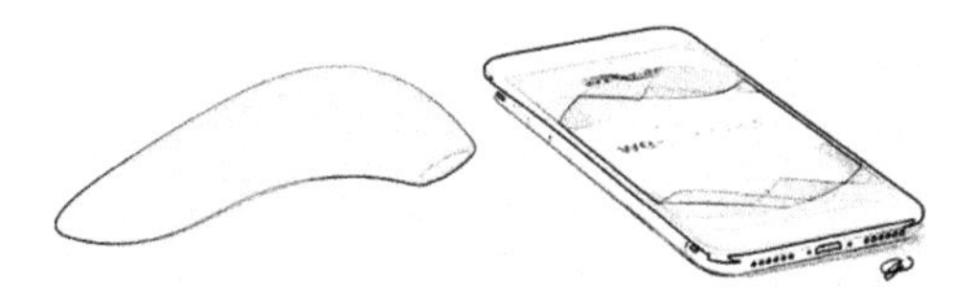

Melt by We-Vibe

Liberator Wedge Intimate Sex Positioning Pillow

This aide raises the pelvis to assist the user in sexual positions such as missionary and doggy style. The Wedge is also helpful for anal and oral sex. This sex pillow provides full-body support and has a 27-degree angle that makes G-spot stimulation easier. The pillow is made of high-density foam and is 14 inches long, 24 inches wide, and 7 inches high.

The soft black microfiber cover is removable and machine-washable and feels soft on the body. The liner is made of polyester and nylon and helps repel moisture. The Liberator Wedge is available in plus size and costs about $79.99.

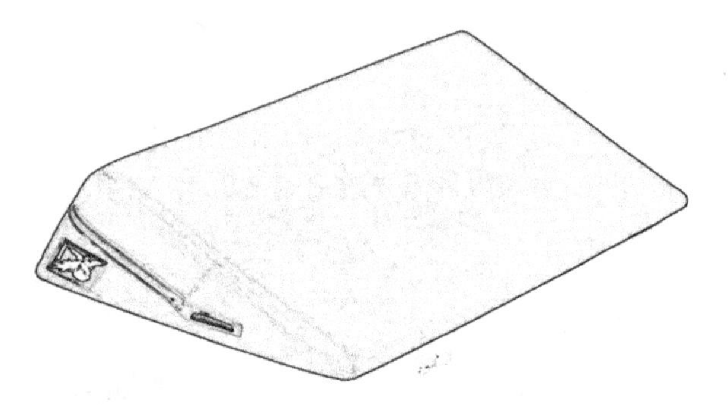

Liberator Wedge Intimate Sex Positioning Pillow

CHAPTER 6

Considerations Before Going to an Adult Sex Store

You'll find that it takes a bit of work to find an affordable body-safe toy that's right for you. This chapter will explain what to look for when choosing a pleasure toy.

Think about substances in pleasure toys.

Soft, flexible pleasure toys are made from silicone, thermoplastic elastomer (TPE), or thermoplastic rubber (TPR). If you want a stronger pleasure toy, pick one that's made of ABS plastic or glass. You can read about the materials used to manufacture pleasure toys and how to test them in Chapter 7.

What characteristics of pleasure toys indicate inferior quality?

Seams and noisy vibrations.

Are pleasure toys expensive?

The price of toys ranges from inexpensive to pricey. Body-safe toys are available to fit everyone's budget.

Are pleasure toys with different dimensions for sale?
Yes. Check the size of dildos, vibrators, or male masturbators. Avoid pleasure toys that are too large or too small.

How can pleasure toys be purchased discreetly?
Remember buying condoms or sanitary napkins for the first time? You may have initially felt embarrassed or uncomfortable, but that feeling eventually went away. You'll soon feel comfortable about visiting an adult sex shop.

Is it better to buy pleasure toys on the Internet or in an adult sex shop?
View pleasure toys online before visiting a brick-and-mortar store. Doing so will help you get used to the variety of choices. Also, keep in mind that small businesses charge more for sex toys because they don't buy in bulk and can't pass on discounts to the consumer. However, these brick-and-mortar stores offer friendly service and education. Ask the salespeople there for information about the sizes, shapes, textures, materials, and stimulating features of the toys. It's okay to ask a lot of questions. And, remember that you can buy pleasure toys at either a brick-and-mortar store or on the Internet.

CHAPTER 7

Pleasure Toy Materials and Testing

Sometimes, customers at a sex shop believe a pleasure toy on the counter or a vibrator with an "eco" stamp must be safe.[86] Descriptions of materials appearing on the outside packages of pleasure toys are often meaningless because the sex toy industry is unregulated. Injuries from adult toys have been steadily rising since 2000 as a result of increased sales.

Sex toy companies aren't required to inform consumers that their products are toxic and unsafe but are obligated to be in compliance with laws regulating electronic parts.

Manufacturers advertise pleasure toys as phthalate-free, body-safe, or made of silicone. On sex toy company websites, silicone is described with terms such as platinum-cured, platinum-grade, medical-grade, body-safe, high quality, 100 percent silicone, and dual density. The sex toy business is lucrative, but body-safe toys from reputable companies are safe.

Why do sex toy manufacturers use so many terms for silicone online?

Companies hope consumers will be gullible enough to believe their ads. That's why they use confusing terms to describe silicone.

For example, a pleasure toy with an FDA-approved silicone label often means that the material is food-grade silicone, which is frequently substituted for medical-grade silicone. As a result, it can be challenging to find body-safe toys. To help you find those toys, I've created a table summarizing the materials used in pleasure toys. The table appears at the end of this chapter.

What makes pleasure toys unsafe?

Bacteria, viruses, and mold grow in the tiny pores of porous pleasure toys, which can't be sterilized and are never spotless even if meticulously washed. For that reason, it's not a good idea to keep a porous toy too long.

Male masturbators or male sleeves for internal use are the only exception. Sex toy companies such as TENGA and Fleshlight produce nontoxic male masturbators.

It's not always safe to use a condom on porous toys to prevent the transmission of sexually transmitted infections (STIs). There have been online reports of chemicals soaking through condoms. Some toys contain mineral oil, which can make condoms decompose.

Avoid any product made with phthalates, chemicals that are used to make toys more flexible, transparent, durable, and long-lasting. Often, inexpensive adult toys are manufactured using these dangerous chemicals. A pleasure toy made from jelly is soft, clear, toxic, and should never be inserted internally. Consumer reports of burning sensations from toxic toys aren't uncommon.[87]

What are signs that a pleasure toy is toxic?

A greasy residue or a shower curtain odor means a toy is toxic and unsafe. Some manufacturers describe toys as being high-quality but sell them for an exceptionally low price. These toys might not be body safe. An inexpensive price probably means it's too good to be true. Amazon.com doesn't indicate if a toy is body safe or where it's made.

How can I find retailers who sell body-safe toys?

Reputable sex toy companies care about consumer safety and have contact information on their websites. These companies maintain a presence in adult stores and have independent reviews. Retailers who care about body-safe toys sell top-quality pleasure toys from trusted manufacturers. You can view Appendix C in this book to find retail brick-and-mortar stores and online shops.

Why are children's toys, child care articles, shower curtains, and food packaging phthalate-free?

Research on animals concludes that phthalates are harmful, damaging kidneys, lungs, developing testes, and the reproductive system. Congress passed the interim Consumer Product Safety Improvement Act (CPSIA) in 2008 to limit the use of three types of phthalates: diethyl hexyl (DEHP), dibutyl phthalate (DBP), and butyl benzyl (BBP). Concentration of phthalates over 0.1 percent in children's toys, child care products, and food packaging is illegal. On April 25, 2018, CPSIA became permanent.[88]

Why are phthalates allowed in adult toys?

Pleasure toys are regarded as novelty items and not devices, so those toys aren't regulated.

Which pleasure toy materials are nonporous?

Nonporous body-safe materials include silicone, Pyrex glass, ABS plastic, metal, lucite, specially-treated wood, natural stone, and ceramic.

Characteristics of Silicone

Silicone is generally cloudy-clear and never crystal-clear. Silicone rubber is nontoxic, odorless, tasteless, nonporous, inert, stable at high temperatures, and resistant to chemicals. Silicone's qualities facilitate its use in food and medical-grade applications.

Adult toys that are made from silicone are either solid silicone or are covered with silicone skin, as is the case with plastic vibrators. Vibrators made of silicone are warm and smooth. All types of silicones aren't the same, though. Some are soft, and others can be unusually hard. The hardness of dildos is measured by a higher shore durometer with scores ranging from extremely soft to quite soft, as well as to squishy firmness.

How will you know if a pleasure toy is made of silicone?

When you unwrap a silicone toy, you might smell a manufacturing odor. But, after you air it out, you'll find that no scent remains. An adult toy with a strong plastic odor that is similar to a new car smell most likely contains chemicals. Pleasure toys covered with a slick film and exhibiting color changes are indicative of plasticizers or chemicals bleeding out.

The shape, size, thickness, and color pigment mix of a toy can determine if the silicone can be stretched to make it turn white. Trained people who work in production and quality assurance can determine the silicone's quality by its stretch and whiteness.

Types of Silicone

Medical-Grade Silicone

Medical grade, or medical-health care grade, class VI silicone is used in a variety of medical applications, including catheters, feeding tubes, implants, gels, condoms, respiratory masks, menstrual cups, and baby bottle nipples. The FDA performs tissue and animal tests on medical-grade silicone to provide safety and efficacy information. This material is also known as platinum-cured silicone.

Medical-grade silicone is stiff, dry, and expensive to manufacture. Raw platinum-cured silicone is more expensive and becomes more so because it requires a longer curing and manufacturing process. Factories need more time and more money to produce medical-grade silicone.

Some writers claim that medical-grade silicone is not feasible for use in casting toys. Several manufacturers adopt the term medical-grade silicone to describe their toy materials. Products viewed as safe can lead to more revenue.

Food-Grade Silicone

This grade of silicone is tested to meet FDA standards for food safety. Food-grade silicone is used in food processing, silicone baking trays, packaging, and preparation applications. It's also found in laboratory and medical environments.

Food-grade silicone is tested to ensure that chemicals from silicone aren't transmitted into heated or cooled food and are safe for mucous membranes. During the tests, a sample is immersed into ethyl alcohol, water, oil, and acetone to determine if harmful substances come out of the material. No research is available about food-grade silicone's effect on humans.

Many companies create safe adult toys from food-grade silicone and claim their products are body-safe and/or medical-grade. Without regulations, this statement is useless. Products advertised as medical-grade silicone sound better than food-grade silicone.

What are the similarities between medical-grade silicone and food-grade silicone?

Both are nontoxic. Good quality controls are applied to manufacturing both types of products.

Medical-grade silicone is regulated by the FDA and the European Union (EU). The FDA, EU, and the BfR (German Federal Institute for Risk Assessment, also known as the Bundesinstitut fur Risikowbewertung) regulate food-grade silicone.

How do medical-grade silicone and food-grade silicone differ?

Medical-grade silicone is cured with platinum, and food-grade silicone is cured with tin. Medical-grade silicone has a greater temperature and chemical durability than food-grade silicone. It's also more expensive to manufacture than food-grade silicone.

Products made from medical-grade silicone last longer than those made from food-grade silicone. Medical-grade silicone doesn't shrivel or become fragile, but food-grade silicone begins to break down over time.

Animal testing on medical-grade silicone is required because its products are used inside the body. Animal testing on food-grade silicone isn't required because it's developed for contact with food only. Medical-grade silicone is slightly cloudy, but there's a higher degree of cloudiness in food-grade silicone.

It's best to wear a condom over a pleasure toy made of food-grade silicone to prevent any possible health risks. Avoid using novelty condoms because they might not be FDA-approved for protection against sexually transmitted infections (STIs).

Platinum-Cured Silicone

The term, platinum-grade silicone, often appears on websites of sex toy companies. Platinum is not a grade. Platinum-cured silicone, the most chemically stable silicone, is made of a base liquid silicone and is cured with a catalyst made of active silicone oil and platinum. Accelerated by heat, silicone becomes a rubber-like elastomer. Platinum-cured silicone toys are the least likely to warp, tear, and bubble.

Sex toy companies such as Tantus, Happy Valley, Vixen Creations, and LELO claim their pleasure toys meet platinum-grade silicone standards. Other companies have products with a silicone label but don't indicate whether they are cured with platimum or tin. View Appendix D in this book for a list of reputable pleasure toy manufacturers.

100-Percent Pure Silicone

Sometimes called platinum silicone on websites, this material is nonporous and nontoxic. A toy that is entirely made of silicone is body safe.

Dual-Density Silicone

Dual-density silicone is composed of a firm layer within the dildo and a soft outer layer, making the pleasure toy comfortable and realistic.

Silicone is firm and flexible and is the best material to use in dual-density toys or dongs, a slang term for penis. Many users prefer dual-density dildos. The glans, or head, of the dildo is spongy, performing as a shock absorber. Vaginal walls are not hit hard by the dildo during vigorous penetration.

The dong, a phallic-shaped toy, can be used for masturbation or as a strap on, simultaneously stimulating two females. The soft outer layer of the dong reduces the impact when strap-on play becomes too energetic. Dongs are also made from thermoplastic rubber, (TPR) or elastomer rubber (TPE) material. Both types of material are porous.

How do you know if a pleasure toy is single density or dual density?

To determine if a dildo is dual density, check the end of the product title for text that reads, 02. For example, the Luke O2 dildo is designed for penetration, but the Adam O2 dildo is slightly curved to target the G-spot. Tantus, a sex toy company, develops superior dual-density dildos for purchase at Adulttoymegastore, USA.

What is Bioskin?

Made of 100% silicone material, Bioskin was patented by a sex toy company, Fun Toys London. This company produces the GJack and GPlug, toys that are covered with Bioskin. This company claims that Bioskin is "as close to the human body as possible." However, one writer disagrees with this statement, suggesting that dual-density silicone dildos feel more realistic.

Although Bioskin is very flexible and spongy, its shape is maintained indefinitely. Bioskin is body safe and nonporous. Between the outer silicone layer and the mechanical core is a spongy, memory-foam layer that is believed to be a type of elastomer. However, the GPlug and the GJack are safe because the silicone coating completely covers these pleasure toys.

Other Materials Used to Produce Pleasure Toys

ABS Plastic

Pleasure toys made from ABS plastic (acrylonitrile butadiene styrene) are inexpensive but not inferior. Some hard plastics are porous unless made from ABS plastic, which has no odor or taste. ABS plastic is smooth, nonporous, phthalate-free, hypoallergenic, and extremely durable. With proper care, these toys can last for years.

Pyrex Glass

Also referred to as borosilicate glass, Pyrex glass is smooth, solid, hard, heavy, nonporous, phthalate-free, hypoallergenic, and resistant to many chemicals. Pleasure toys made from Pyrex glass provide hot and cold sensations and have a high melting point. Compared to silicone, Pyrex glass toys apply more robust pressure to the G-spot or to the prostate gland.

Pyrex glass is incredibly tough and strong because it's made through the annealing process, which is a lengthy process of cooking glass slowly. This process removes internal stress. The pleasure toy user slips a finger through the Pyrex glass pull loop and easily removes an anal toy out of the anus.[89]

Metal

Most metal toys are composed of stainless steel or aluminum. Some luxury toys are made from gold and silver. Crowned Jewels UK is an excellent brand for safe aluminum toys.

Stainless steel toys are strong, smooth, nonporous, phthalate-free, heavy, and perfect for exercising vaginal PC muscles. Expensive chrome-plated steel dildos are hard, firm, and durable. Anyone who wants different temperature sensations can warm or cool a steel dildo in water.

You can buy safe toys consisting of medical-grade stainless steel from Njoy Toys. Their dildos are popular for role-playing in BDSM (bondage, discipline or domination, sadism, and masochism).

Users of erotic electrostimulation, also known as electrosex, apply electrical stimulation to the genitals. Violet wands are frequently used in BDSM and provide low current, high voltage, and high-frequency electricity to deliver sharp or piercing sensations.

Lucite

Lucite, the best version of acrylic, is a hard, glass-like, durable material composed of methyl methacrylate, a transparent, thermoplastic plastic. Pleasure toys made from Lucite are light and less likely to fracture. These toys can be heated and cooled.

People with allergies purchase acrylic toys because they are nonporous, nontoxic, and phthalate-free. This material has a smooth surface that glides against sensitive skin. This quality is ideal for dildos, wands, G-spot stimulators, prostate massagers, and cock rings.

Treated Wood

Pleasure toys made from wood are unique and beautiful. Treated wood — sealed mechanically with nontoxic, solvent-free water and medical-grade varnish — is nonporous, safe, and glides with a small amount of lubricant. A high-quality finish makes the grain look three-dimensional. Most wood makers spend a great deal of time sanding toys to eliminate coarse spots and sharp edges.

For safety reasons, wooden toys aren't stained. A natural finish can wear off rapidly, making wooden toys vulnerable to moisture retention that causes swelling, splinters, and porous characteristics. Avoid stained toys or those with a natural finish.

The toxicity of treated wooden toys is determined by the coating used by the manufacturer. The salad bowl finish used on hardwood dildos is food safe.

The sex toy manufacturer, NobEssence, applies Lubrosity, an excellent coating containing a medical-grade polymer used on medical devices, to highlight the loveliness of the wood grain. This company's toys are hypoallergenic and resistant to bacteria and moisture.

Natural Stones

According to the Gemological Institute of America (GIA), quartz, rose quartz, and amethyst stones are nonporous. Many natural stone toys are polished and can't be sealed. This affects porosity. Natural stone toys that are inserted in the body for long-term use might not be safe.

Other factors affect the porosity of these single-crystal materials. For example, the quench crackling process heats crystals, making stones porous and less safe. Fractures are caused by putting natural stones in water and then by placing them in a container with dye that changes the color of the stones. The next procedure fills the cracks with polymer that might make the stone safer to use on the body.

The sex toy industry doesn't regulate the manufacturing process of natural stone dildos. For that reason, you should place a condom over a crystal stone toy to protect against germs. Some people may argue that healing powers are lost when the crystal is covered, but it's safer to follow medical science than mystical beliefs.

Ceramic

The kiln-firing and glazing processes produce safe, nonporous toys by heating ceramic to a liquid form. The material is then cooled quickly to produce a vitrified solid and water-resistant final product.

Ceramic toys don't tolerate sudden heat changes. Check with a lead testing kit to ensure that the glazing process doesn't produce lead. And, don't use a toy that has flaws.

Should condoms be used with pleasure toys?

Yes. Condoms help prevent the transmission of bacteria.

Which types of condoms can be worn on toys made with nonporous silicone or hard materials?

Most lubricated condoms use an inexpensive silicone lube that can damage silicone toys.

Non-lubricated condoms or water-based lubricated condoms are compatible with toys made of silicone.

Are novelty condoms safe?

No. These condoms might not be FDA-approved for effective prevention of pregnancy and STIs.

Which sex toy materials should be avoided?

PVC

Pleasure toys made from polyvinyl chloride (PVC) are commonplace, inexpensive, and highly porous. PVC is a plastic. Vinyl chloride, which is used to produce PVC, is on Canada's Toxic Substances List and has been classified as a carcinogen. Don't buy a realistic dildo made from PVC that has been softened by phthalates.

Jelly and Latex Rubber

Jelly and latex rubber products are extraordinarily porous and toxic, containing phthalates, which are dangerous chemicals. This material is characterized by smell, stickiness, transparency, and bright colors. Latex rubber toys often cause allergic reactions.[90,91]

Realistic Materials Such as Cyberskin, Pure Skin, and Realskin

Realistic materials aren't part of a class of materials but rather instead are designated as a description.

Initially, a hard plastic, mineral oil, or phthalates are added to thermoplastics to soften realistic pleasure toys, simulating real skin. Unstable, realistic materials eventually disintegrate over time and release a strong odor and an oily residue.

Anyone who is allergic to mineral oil might have a reaction and should avoid buying pleasure toys made with thermoplastics. Some pleasure toys are developed from PVC, TPR, rubber, and many other unsafe materials. Paint, for example, is added to color the veins in dildos that eventually fades away.

Softer pleasure toys contain more chemicals, making the products more porous. So, realistic materials aren't safe for everyone. The reason is that soft skin synthetic materials make ultra-realistic dildos and vibrators unusually porous and possibly toxic. These pleasure toys are more likely to rip and tear than those made of silicone.

Pure Skin is made from thermoplastic elastomer (TPE) and feels like real human skin. Several comparable materials have brand names such as PleasureSkin, Trueskin, Cyberskin, Realskin, and Techno-Skin. Cyberskin is safe to use in packing and is worn externally to give the appearance of a penis.

Realistic Materials Such as Ultra Realistic (UR3) and Sensa-Firm

Both types of realistic material are phthalate-free and hypoallergenic. Ultra-Realistic Skin (UR3) is made by combining PVC and silicone. The soft, silky finish of a dildo can resemble human skin. The toy produces stimulations that mimic being with a partner. UR3 is safer than Sensa-Firm for men and women who have allergies and sensitivities.

Sensa-Firm, a thermal plastic elastomer, is a type of rubber used to make vibrators, dildos, and butt plugs. This product is soft, porous, and resembles human skin.

Elastomer (rubber)

Elastomer (rubber) varieties include thermoplastic elastomer (TPE) or thermoplastic rubber (TPR). These elastomers are also referred to as skin-safe rubber, and they become warm with friction and feel soft to the touch with elasticity like human skin.

A pleasure toy made with TPE and TPR is the safest product on the avoid list. Some toy companies advertise medical-grade TPE as nonporous. In some cases, this is true. But, toys must be analyzed to determine the accuracy of these claims. The danger of porous TPE toys is retention of the human papilloma virus (HPV). You can prevent the transmission of HPV by wearing a condom. For people ranging in age from 9 to 45 years old, the HPV vaccine is also an option.

Why do sex toy manufacturers use PVC, latex, and rubber in pleasure toys?

PVC, latex, and rubber toys are cheap to produce. A condom must be worn on these sex products.

What kind of condom should be worn with porous toys?

Buy polyurethane and non-latex condoms for use with porous toys. Polyurethane condoms are thinner than latex condoms and can be used with lubricants that are oil based or water based. Polyurethane condoms also transmit heat, enhancing pleasure for some people who like warm sensations. These condoms have little or no smell and last longer than latex condoms. Manufacturers recommend that people wear condoms when sharing pleasure toys with partners.

Silicone Composite Toys

Unlike toys made of 100-percent silicone, inexpensive silicone composite toys are porous and toxic. Sil-A-Gel's appearance is gel-like when softened with polyvinyl chloride (PVC). Some retailers think Sil-A-Gel is silicone. But it actually contains less than 10-percent silicone. Don't buy toys made with mixtures of silicone or Sil-A-Gel.

Vinyl

Toxic phthalates are often added to vinyl to soften toys.[92]

Soda-Lime Glass

This inexpensive glass contains sodium oxide (soda) and calcium oxide (lime). Soda-lime glass shatters readily and is three times less resistant to extreme temperature changes than borosilicate glass or Pyrex.

Loops on toys made from soda-lime glass have weak spots and break easily, and cheap soda lime glass is used to make toys in China. In addition, online sex toy companies such as Lovehoney and Pipedream sell glass dildos made from soda-lime. Amazon.com sells questionably made toys, too. The giant shopping website sells glass dildos covered with a varnish containing toxic metals such as lead and cadmium. Avoid painted glass toys because paint can leach toxins including arsenic and mercury into the skin and body.

Sex Toy Testing

Tests provide evidence that pleasure toys are body safe.

Ash Test

To conduct an ash test, burn part of the silicone pleasure toy. Medical-or food-grade silicone won't continue to flame or melt. If a pale gray ash remains, then the toy is made of silicone. But, to avoid getting burned, don't get too close to the flame.

If the pleasure toy isn't made of silicone, there will be a lack of gray ash after you burn part of the toy. If you need to use water to douse the flame created by burning the toy, that's another indication that the toy isn't made of silicone. Such a toy will also appear to be melted and have distorted and charred black material.

Flame Test

Jelly toys contain benzene, a flammable substance. Put a flame to the dildo to determine whether the product is composed of jelly. But, don't get too close to the flame.

Lick Test

Lick a toy. If your tongue becomes numb, then the toy is dangerous. An experienced person can identify phthalates.

Polariscope Test

Buy a Polariscope on Amazon for $30 to determine if a glass toy is properly annealed. The test indicates whether glass has been cooled correctly. Pleasure toys are clear if the annealing process is done right. Weaker toys show rainbow colors. Check toys for cracks.

Lead Test

You can buy basic lead testing equipment to determine whether a pleasure toy contains lead. A glass toy with a varnish coating contains lead.

Guidelines on Selecting Safe Pleasure Toys

It's safe to buy nonporous adult toys that aren't toxic.[93] Avoid all toxic porous toys. You can buy nontoxic nonporous toys from reliable sex toy companies and sex shops.

How will a consumer know if a dildo is body-safe?

The surfaces of nonporous toys are smooth and water-resistant. A dildo made from annealed borosilicate glass is safe.[94] Only two "skin-like" types of materials made by Tantus O2 and Vixen Creations VixSkin are phthalate-free, nonporous, and can be sterilized.[95]

A dildo that is transparent, flexible, and supple is most likely toxic and is made softer by adding phthalates. A small number of safe dildos made from elastomers don't contain phthalates but are still porous and can't be sterilized. These toys are never clean, even when washed frequently. If dildos are inexpensive, they might very well be toxic. When people use such toys, they may experience burning sensations, rashes, and blistering. The severity of the resulting burns will be determined by the frequency of use and amount of phthalates in the toy.

Don't use a dildo in anal intercourse. You should also avoid unflared anal toys that get stuck in the rectum. Such toys may result in a trip to the emergency room. Chinese manufacturers sell anal toys on Amazon.com that should be classified as dildos.[96]

What should be done with a pleasure toy collection that is porous and toxic?

Throw it out. Buy safe pleasure toys made from 100-percent silicone, platinum-cured silicone, stainless steel, ABS plastic, Pyrex glass, aluminum, ceramics, natural stone, and wood.

Table 1: Pleasure Toy Materials

Material	Nonporous	Phthalate-free	Toxic	Hypoallergenic	Condoms
Silicone	X	X		X	Non-lubricated water-based
Silicone composite					Polyurethane
ABS Plastic	X	X		X	Latex
Pyrex Glass a.k.a borosilicate glass	X	X		X	Latex
Treated Wood	X	X	Depends on coating used by manufac-turer	X	Latex
Crystal Stones	Depends on treatment process	X			Latex
Ceramic	Depends on treatment process				Latex
Metal Stainless Steel Aluminum	X	X		X	Latex
Lucite	X	X		X	Polyurethane
PVC			Contains toxic vinyl chloride		Polyurethane
Jelly and latex rubber			X		Polyurethane
Realistic Materials Cyberskin, Realskin			Possibly toxic		Polyurethane

CHAPTER 8

Personal Lubricants

Lubricants reduce friction, prevent irritation, and enhance sexual activity. Though the Food and Drug Administration (FDA) doesn't regulate pleasure toys, the FDA regulates lubricants. But, are lubricants safe? The World Health Organization (WHO) and other researchers guide users of personal lubricants to select safe ones, which are listed in Appendix E in this book.

The consumer must decide whether to use a personal lubricant that is silicone-based, water-based, oil-based, hybrid, natural, or organic. Some ingredients in lubricants don't work well with everyone's body chemistry. When applied to pleasure toys and condoms, the wrong lubricant can damage those toys and condoms. To view a summary of lubricants that can safely be applied to pleasure toy materials and condoms, view the table at the end of this chapter.

How does the FDA oversee personal lubricants (sex aids)?

The Federal Food, Drug, and Cosmetic Act (FD&C Act) of 1938 urged the FDA to enforce a "reasonable assurance of safety and effectiveness" before a sex aid is marketed. In 1976, the FDA listed over-the-counter vaginal lubricants as Class II medical devices when used for medical purposes. Such purposes can include lubricating the vagina to insert a diagnostic or therapeutic device.

Only recently, did the FDA extend the Class II medical device requirement to personal lubricants. However, many lubricants on the market don't have 510(k) clearance or a premarket notification. This comprehensive safety process involves testing personal lubricants on rabbits and guineapigs. Animal testing doesn't have to be performed on a personal lubricant if a company finds a similar alternative.

The FDA's method of classification is confusing. Personal lubricants advertised as moisturizers or cleansers are categorized as cosmetics and have lower safety standards. Some are categorized as drugs if composed of specified ingredients or affect functions of the human body.

The FDA views rectal use of lubes as an "off-label" application. Such an application means that you're using it at your own risk.

What's the difference between lubricants and moisturizers?

Moisturizers are applied a few times a week. Polymers stick to cells and keep water in place on vaginal surfaces. Moisturizers are designed to provide lasting relief from dryness and are sloughed off after a few days. Lubricants stay on the surface of the skin, providing relief from dryness. You can use them at the beginning of sex or during sex.

Why do people use lubricants?

Vaginal dryness or inadequate natural lubrication can result from aging, menopause, breastfeeding, diabetes, inflammatory bowel disease, the side effects of cancer treatments, or some medications. Lubricants reduce the chance of vaginal tearing. This type of tearing increases the risk of contracting STIs including HIV.

Men use lubricants when using masturbation sleeves. Those who engage in anal sex with or without pleasure toys and fisting require additional lubrication. Overall, lubricants enhance sex play.

How many people in the U.S. use personal lubricants? And how much money is spent on lubes in the U.S.?

The U.S. Census data and Simmons National Consumer Survey (NHCS) published in 2019 reported that 49.92 million Americans purchased personal lubricants, spending $219 million in 2018.[97]

What's the value of personal lubricants in the global market?

Research from the Symphony IRI Group stated that the global-market for personal lubricants was worth $894 million in 2018 and predicts a compound annual growth rate (CAGR) of 8.1% from 2019-2026.[98]

What does the research indicate about why people use personal lubricants?

About 65 percent of 1,021 women in the United States report that vaginal lubricants make sexual activity more comfortable, fun, and enjoyable and lessen discomfort and pain.[99]

Out of 1,014 men who participated in an online questionnaire sponsored by the National Survey of Sexual Health and Behavior, 70 percent used personal lubricants. Participants reported that personal lubricants make sex more comfortable, fun, and their partners want them to use a lube.[100]

In the same survey, over 90 percent of 332 gay males and 101 bisexual males indicated that lubricants make anal sex comfortable and pleasurable. Curiosity and a desire to reduce pain and discomfort are other reasons that lubes are used in sex play.[101]

How do pH and osmolality levels affect the safety of personal lubricants?

The pH of a lubricant indicates whether it's acidic or alkaline. Healthy pH levels of the vagina range from 3.8 to 4.5. Many personal lubricants with pH levels exceeding 4.5 correlate to a greater risk for bacterial vaginosis and HIV. The rectum's pH level is close to 7, and a rectal lubricant should range from 5.5 to 7.

Osmolality is a substance's ability to draw moisture from tissues and cells. Female vaginal secretions have a normal range of 260 to 290 mOsm/kg. Male semen has a normal range of 250 to 380 mOsm/kg. A lubricant with a higher osmolality or hyperosmolality shrinks vaginal tissue. Hyperosmolality results in skin irritation and disrupts the mucous membrane barrier, leading to loss of the vagina's protection from infection. Rectal use of lubricants with high osmolality levels may increase susceptibility to HIV infection.

Many personal lubes with hyperosmolality contain large amounts of moisturizers, glycerin, and propylene glycol. Without them, a water-based lube evaporates quickly, causing a cold sensation.

Most lubricants have high osmolality levels from 2000 to 6000 mOsm/kg, increasing risk for STIs, including HIV. The World Health Organization (WHO) suggests using a lubricant with a pH level of 4.5 and osmolality below 380 mOsm/kg.[102] At present, the acceptable osmolality rating is 1200 mOsm/kg.

View Appendix E in this book for lists of lubricant brand names, manufacturers, pH levels, and osmolality ratings from the WHO and researchers. You can also contact manufacturers to determine whether preferred brands that aren't on the list meet WHO requirements for pH levels and osmolality.

What is the research on vaginal lubricants?

Research findings on whether personal lubricants cause skin irritations are mixed. One study concluded that hyperosmolar glycerin in lubricants causes damage to vaginal and rectal tissue that can lead to bacterial vaginosis. The vaginal flora is altered and leads to a higher transmission rate of STIs.[103] Some small studies support these findings.

Normal vaginal flora or bacteria living inside the vagina are predominantly lactobacilli, which keep the vagina healthy and prevent the growth of yeast. An increase in vaginal pH leads to bacteria in the vagina instead of lactobacilli.

Hyperosmolar lubricant gels were correlated with cellular toxicity and epithelial damage while showing no anti-viral activity. This study indicated that Gynol II, a vaginal contraceptive gel, KY Jelly, a personal lubricant and Replens, a moisturizer were toxic to lactobacillus. This research also concluded that silicone-based lubes, Female Condom 2 lubricant and Wet Platinum, and two water-based lubes, Pre-seed (Fertility-Friendly lubricant) and Good Clean Love, are the safest.[104]

A study testing K-Y Warming gel with high glycerin levels showed no harm to the vaginal flora in rhesus monkeys. Researchers from the Kinsey Institute reviewed participants' reports of skin irritation with and without applying lubes on their genitals. Some women report more irritations when not utilizing lubricants during sex. Tests of lubes containing glycerin and propylene glycol don't indicate any problems.[105.106]

None of these research studies definitively conclude that personal lubricants directly cause infections. WHO advises women to select a pH and osmolality balanced lube. This type of lube is physiologically comparable to vaginal secretions.[107]

Is it important to use lubricants for anal sex? What research is available on lubes used in anal intercourse?

Lubricants are essential for anal activities. The reason is that the anus doesn't self-lubricate like the vagina, and anal walls are thinner than vaginal walls. Thicker lubes should be used during anal sex to avoid injuries that include cuts and rips. Such injuries can increase the risk of contracting a sexually transmitted infection (STI).

Anal intercourse is riskier for STI transmission than vaginal sex or oral sex. People who use lubricants in anal intercourse are more likely to develop gonorrhea or chlamydia.[108] That's why condoms should be worn during anal sex. Use a lubricant that is compatible with latex condoms. Monogamous partners who have been tested for STIs may decide not to wear condoms.

Water-based lubricants cause the anus to absorb water rapidly and dry out. Silicone-based lubes are best for anal intercourse but destroy pleasure toys made from silicone. Use plenty of water-based lube with silicone toys.

Is the amount of each ingredient in personal lubes shown on the label?

The FDA doesn't require that the quantity of each ingredient be listed on the package. Generally, ingredients supplied in the greatest quantity in the product will appear first on the label.

Which ingredients in lubricants should you avoid?

Synthetic preservatives and chemicals cause irritation of vaginal mucous membranes that lead to genital rashes. People who have sensitive skin or allergies or are prone to yeast infections should avoid lubes containing parabens, petroleum, glycerin and other sugars, synthetic chemicals, dyes, preservatives, artificial fragrances, animal-based ingredients, or toxins. A lube containing latex can cause people with latex allergies to experience irritations.

Parabens were introduced in the 1950s to prolong the shelf life of cosmetics and to prevent the growth of mold and bacteria. A 2004 study indicated that parabens could be linked to breast cancer tumors, developmental disorders, fertility problems, and chronic diseases. The American Cancer Society (ACA) reported that this study didn't demonstrate that parabens correlate to breast cancer tumors because it has insufficient estrogen properties.

The FDA and the ACA report that small amounts of parabens in cosmetics don't cause harm, but both organizations recommend avoiding products with high amounts of parabens.

Dr. Alyssa Dweck, an OB-GYN and co-author of the book, *The Complete A to Z for Your V*, informs patients, especially those with estrogen-sensitive breast cancer, to avoid lubes that contain parabens.

Check the labels of lubes for the most frequently listed paraben ingredients, including butylparaben, methylparaben, and propylparaben.

Phenoxyethanol, a hazardous chemical preservative, is found in perfumes and insect repellent and causes skin irritations and toxicity.

Propylene glycol is a toxic chemical that is used as a preservative in food, tobacco, electronic cigarettes, and in a few brands of antifreeze. This substance may cause skin irritations, burning, and pain in some women.

Chlorhexidine gluconate, an antibacterial agent utilized in antiseptics and in multipurpose lubricants, causes irritation and destroys strains of lactobacillus, which are the bacteria found in a healthy vagina.

Glycerin — a type of sugar found in sweeteners, low-fat foods, and liqueurs — increases vaginal yeast infections in women.

Animal studies have shown that a silicone-based lubricant containing Cyclomethicone, Cyclopentasiloxane, and Cyclotetrasiloxane may harm the reproductive system and cause uterine cancer. Unfortunately, research about the long-term effects on women's vaginas is nonexistent.

What are the pros and cons of using saliva as a lubricant?

Saliva is available and free but not harmless. It evaporates and dries up quickly, and it's not slippery. Using spit as a makeshift lube does not reduce friction during penile-vaginal intercourse and can cause small tears in the vagina. Pain and irritations provide an opening for pathogens.

Saliva is the most frequent way genital herpes is transmitted to a partner. Dr. Felice Gersh, a gynecologist, believes that 99.9 percent of people who use spit as a lubricant risk getting STIs, yeast infections, or bacterial vaginosis. Sex partners who have herpes, gonorrhea, chlamydia, HPV, syphilis, and trichomoniasis may be asymptomatic too.

Which household products shouldn't be used as lubricants?

Don't use household products such as baby oil, petroleum jelly, or Vaseline as lubricants. Studies indicate that baby oil increases the risk of yeast infections. Petroleum or petroleum-based ingredients (Vaseline) creates the illusion of moisturized skin but actually prevent moisture from leaving the skin. Women who use Vaseline as a lubricant are 2.2 times more likely to be infected with bacterial vaginosis.[109] Baby oil and Vaseline are greasy and difficult to wash off the body, sheets, and clothing.

Vegetable oil, canola oil, and other refined oils that undergo heating, bleaching, and chemical treatments shouldn't be used as lubricants. These household products destroy pleasure toys.

Which household products shouldn't be used with latex condoms?

Baby oil, burn ointment, dairy butter, palm oil or coconut oil, cooking oil, fish oil, mineral oil, suntan oil, hemorrhoid cream, petroleum jelly (Vaseline), and body/hand lotion.[110]

Do latex condoms cause burning, itching, and irritation?

Yes. If you experience frequent and unexplained itching after penile-vaginal intercourse, it may be a sign of an allergic reaction to the condom or to the spermicide. Although it's possible to be sensitive to any type of condom, latex is most often culpable.

Why avoid fragrances in personal lubricants?

People with sensitive skin who use lubes with fragrances may develop rashes, allergic reactions, and irritations in the vagina.

Why should novelty lubes not be purchased?

Avoid novelty lubricants advertising "warming" or "tingling" sensations. These lubricants cause vaginal irritation or inflammation.[111] The vagina's pH level differs from a novelty lube's pH level. Some novelty lubes can also cause a chemical reaction with pleasure toys made of rubber.

How can I test the ingredients in lubes to find out if they're safe?

Do a simple patch test before using a new lube for sex play. First, wash one of your arms with unscented soap and pat your arm dry.

Then apply a few drops of the lube on a small patch of your skin, preferably in the crook of your elbow. Afterwards, cover that area of skin with a bandage. After completing all three steps, wait 24 hours and then take off the bandage. If you see redness, swelling, itching, or blistering on your skin, don't use the lube. Sometimes, you'll see a skin reaction in less than 24 hours. Nevertheless, you should use soap and warm water to wash off the lube.

What's the most efficient way to apply lubricants to adult toys?

Warm the lube in your hands and apply an even layer of it on the entire surface of a pleasure toy.

What are the most inefficient ways to apply lubricants?

The user can't see what is being lubricated when fingers insert lube. Relying on sense of touch to determine whether lube is applied evenly is not reliable. This ineffective method is used frequently. Applicators filled with lubricants are inserted into the body, but there is no way to determine if it is adequate.

Which types of lubricants are available?

Silicone-Based Lubes

Silicone lube is odorless, waterproof, and excellent for sex in the shower, as well as for masturbation and anal intercourse. This type of lube can be used as a massage oil and is compatible with pleasure toys made of hard plastics, aluminum, steel, Lucite, ceramic, wood, marble, stone, (granite) and glass.

Silicone lube is incompatible with toys made of silicone. The reason is that silicone bonds to silicone and turns costly pleasure toys into a sticky mess. Softer pleasure toys containing jelly or Cyberskin deteriorate when silicone lube is applied on them.

Apply water-based lubricant to silicone toys. Silicone lube is compatible with latex condoms.

Dimethicone and Cyclomethicone are the main ingredients of silicone lube and are indicated on the label. The latter is being replaced by Cyclopentasiloxane in most silicone lubricants. Dimethicone, the most expensive and highest-grade manufactured silicone oil, is FDA-approved and should be the first ingredient listed. Use hypoallergenic silicone-based lubricant on extremely sensitive skin.

Lather two or three drops of silicone lube in your hands and apply it to pleasure toys. It's not necessary to reapply silicone lube during sexual activity because it lasts longer than water-based lubricants. Too much silicone lube stains sheets, though. Clean the sheets with a grease removing detergent or soap and water.

Applying premium-grade silicone lube to platinum-cured silicone toys isn't a guarantee of safety. For that reason, you should conduct a spot test by putting one or two drops of the lube on the base of your pleasure toy. Then wait a few minutes to see if the lube stays slick. If the lube sticks and is difficult to extract from the toy, don't use the lube on the toy.

Some lubes may damage Godemiche toys, which are made from premium platinum-cured silicone and are manufactured in Germany. These pleasure toys are custom-made, color-coated, and available for a reasonable price. Godemiche reports that Give Lube Silicone, Silicone+, Uber Lube, Spunk, ID Millennium and Pjur ORIGINAL are compatible with their toys.

Water-Based Lubes

Water-based lube has a thicker consistency than most lubes, making them friction-free. It's available in gels, creams, and liquids and doesn't stain sheets because of the high water content.

Water-based lubes also dry quickly, can be sticky, aren't hypoallergenic, and must be reapplied during sex play. Water-based lubes with high osmolality can dry out vaginal tissue. These lubes are compatible with all toy materials, including silicone and latex condoms. But, if you experience burning, itching or irritation after using the lubes with toys, discontinue use. Avoid inexpensive brands of lubes containing paraben and glycerin that may cause irritations. People with sensitive skin should test water-based lubricants prior to use.

Oil-Based Lubes

Similar to silicone, oil lubes last longer, retain heat with friction, and are pleasurable when used during masturbation, foreplay, and massages.

Keep in mind that oil lubes aren't hypoallergenic. So, if you have sensitive skin, test the lube on your hand or arm before using a larger amount. And, remember that this lube can cover the vagina and anus. That means you'll need more time to clean the lube off your skin and pleasure toys.

Oil lube is compatible with most pleasure toy materials except Lucite. However, this lubricant isn't compatible with latex condoms, which provide the best protection against transmission of STIs. Many studies state that latex condoms deteriorate within one minute of exposure to oil lubes.

Partners who are in committed relationships and test negative for STIs usually don't wear condoms and can use oil lubricants. If deciding to use condoms, be aware that lambskin condoms don't prevent the transmission of STIs including HIV.

Hybrid Lubes

Hybrid lubes, a mixture of silicone and water-based formulas, last longer than water-based lubes but aren't as thick as silicone lubes. Most hybrid lubes contain a little silicone, possibly damaging toys made of silicone unless washed immediately after use. This type of lube is compatible with latex condoms.

Natural Lubricants

Are natural lubricants organic?

Words such as organic and natural are often used to market products, but consumers still have trouble knowing what to buy. For example, even though a lube with coconut oil might be considered natural because the oil originates from fruit, the coconuts aren't considered organic after being sprayed with pesticides. The United States Department of Agriculture (USDA) certifies lubes as organic when the ingredients don't come in contact with chemicals such as pesticides, artificial fertilizers, hormones, and GMOs (genetically modified organisms). And, AH! YES products such as aloe vera, sunflower seed oil, and vitamin E oil are certified as organic.

Ingredients in natural lubes aren't certified, but natural lubes that imitate natural vaginal or rectal secretions are the best. You should choose a lubricant that contains very few ingredients. You'll find that the ingredients are much more likely to be natural if they're easy to pronounce.

Which natural household products shouldn't be used as lubricants?

Some people report using egg whites as lubricants, but doctors don't recommend putting egg whites in the vagina. There's simply not enough evidence showing that doing so is safe.

Aloe vera, a natural substance that has been around for centuries, is used for health, medicinal, and beauty purposes and is known for soothing sunburned skin. However, applying aloe vera to the genitals can result in redness, burning, a stinging sensation, a rash, and allergic reactions.

Yogurt, another household product, has been used as a lubricant and as a treatment for yeast infections. Some people even believe that the probiotics in unflavored and sugarless yogurt maintain normal bacteria in the vagina. But, scientists haven't determined if that belief is accurate and don't recommend inserting yogurt into the vagina.

Similarly, it's not a good idea to use butter as a lubricant. Butter contains casein proteins from milk, which can become rancid.

Which natural household products can be used as lubricants?

Unrefined virgin coconut oil is antifungal and antibacterial, prevents yeast infections, and helps with vaginal dryness. This oil is terrific in cooking, makes hair shiny and healthy, and can be used as a general moisturizer. Unrefined virgin coconut oil also provides a wonderful feeling inside the vagina and has a delicious aroma and flavor.

In warm weather, coconut oil turns to liquid and stains sheets. The solution is to put liquid coconut oil in a squeeze bottle or pump bottle.

Sweet almond oil can be used to moisturize sensitive skin. Best of all, this oil is safe to eat, lasts a long time, smells nice, and is perfect for oral and anal sex.

Olive oil and avocado oil are terrific for use as moisturizers and can reduce friction but should be washed off right away to prevent clogged pores. Use a liquid dropper to apply the amount of oil needed.

Ghee, a type of clarified butter frequently used in South Asian cooking, is becoming known for its healing properties.

Ghee moisturizes and soothes the skin, provides healthy fatty acids, tastes wonderful, and is perfect for oral sex. But, Ghee should be washed off before turning rancid.

Nagaimo — a yam that's popular in China, Japan, and Vietnam — is slippery and slimy in texture and can be used as a lube when mixed with coconut oil.

Aloe Cadabra is a lubricant and moisturizer that consists of 95 percent organic aloe vera and is marketed as being natural, which isn't entirely true. The remaining ingredients are vitamin E oil, xanthan, citric acid, potassium sorbate, sodium benzoate, and organic vanilla planifolia concentrate.

Xanthan is a thickening agent. Citric acid regulates the pH levels in lubes to imitate the acidity in the vagina which explains why Aloe Cadabra has an osmolality rating of 172 mOsm/kg. That rating is close to the vagina's osmolality of 260-290mOsm/kg.

Potassium sorbate and sodium benzoate act as preservatives. And organic vanilla planifolia concentrate is a synthetic, lab-pro- duced product that provides the scent of vanilla in the lube.

Can condoms be used with natural household lubricants?

Many natural lubes are oil-based and degrade condoms. Don't use condoms with coconut oil, sweet almond oil, almond oil, olive oil, ghee, and nagaimo.

Do gynecologists recommend any lubes for sexual activity?

Lauren Streicher, associate clinical professor of obstetrics and gynecology at Northwestern University, says there are two criteria for lubes. Among those criteria are whether they're slippery enough and last long enough. Another criterion is whether the lubes cause irritations. Dr. Streicher suggests that silicone-based lubes are the best but can't be used with toys made from silicone.

Table 2: Pleasure Toys — Materials and Lubricants

Material	Silicone Lube	Water-Based Lube	Oil-Based Lube	Hybrid Lube
Silicone		X	X	
Wood	X	X	X	X
Metal	X	X	X	X
ABS Plastic	X	X	X	X
Pyrex Glass	X	X	X	X
Lucite	X	X		X
Jelly Rubber	X	X		
TPR/TPE		X		
Realistic Materials		X		
Condoms	Compatible with latex condoms	Compatible with latex condoms	Incompatible with latex condoms. Use polyurethane or lambskin condoms.	Compatible with latex condoms

CHAPTER 9

Cleaning and Storing Pleasure Toys

In the "Knockoffs" episode of the TV show, *Broad City*, Abbi and her attractive neighbor, Jeremy, have a passionate night trying out pegging. Dan Savage, a journalist, coined this term in 2001 to mean "a woman fucking a man in the ass with a strap-on dildo."

After Jeremy leaves for work the next morning, Abbi decides to tidy up. She washes his dildo in the dishwasher. He comes home to discover the ruined custom-made Shinjo, a high-end pleasure toy. Jeremy is furious at her, and Abbi thinks he's overreacting. The brief affair ends with the dildo's death.[112]

The "Knockoffs" episode shows that pleasure toys should be cleaned properly. Cleaning them properly is not only cost-effective but prevents STIs including HIV. You can find cleaning instructions on your pleasure toy's packaging or on the manufacturer's website. It's important to clean adult toys before and after each use to prevent the transmission of germs in solo or partner sex.

The CDC defines sanitizing as the reduction of germs to a safe level, meeting public health requirements. Disinfection eliminates or lessens harmful germs on surfaces. Sterilization kills all germs and any spores.

You might be wondering how to clean pleasure toys. Effective cleaning, drying, and storing methods depend on whether the materials in pleasure toys are porous, nonporous, non-motorized, motorized, or waterproof. Four tables in this chapter summarize cleaning methods for all pleasure toy materials, making this book an excellent reference.

How do the vagina and penis become infected with pathogens or germs from pleasure toys?

Recurring bacterial vaginosis, yeast infections, itching, redness, and pain in women, and yeast and skin infections in men can occur when partners share unclean toys. Anal toys can transfer *E.coli* bacteria from the rectum to the vagina during sexual intercourse, and *E.coli* is responsible for urinary tract infections.

Why should pleasure toys be cleaned?

Microscopic holes in porous toys capture moisture and provide a refuge for bacteria or other pathogens to grow and survive. Germs live in bodily fluids on hard surfaces for a long time. Elastomer (rubber) varieties such as TPR, TPE, rubber, and jelly rubber are porous and trap bacteria. Skin-safe materials such as Cyberskin, Pure Skin, Realskin, SensaFirm, and Ultra Realistic (UR3) are also porous.

Pleasure toys can transmit STIs including HIV when shared. Bacteria causing gonorrhea live for about 24 hours on hard surfaces. The chlamydia bacterium is only active for a few hours. A fungus causing yeast infections stays alive for weeks. Bacterial vaginosis lives on hard surfaces for one or two days. HIV and the herpes virus don't survive long on surfaces.[113] Ultimately, wearing a condom when playing with a pleasure toy makes the toy easier to clean and prevents bacterial growth.

Bacteria, viruses, and other pathogens usually don't survive on nonporous pleasure toys after those toys have been cleaned and dried. However, the transmission of human papillomavirus (HPV) through shared use of pleasure toys was detected up to 24 hours after standard cleaning.[114]

What are some other benefits from cleaning toys regularly?

Motors are maintained and last much longer.[115]

Is a dishwasher effective at destroying germs?

The National Sanitation Foundation (NSF) certifies dishwashers as meeting sanitization standards when those dishwashers have one of several cycles: SaniWash, sanitize, or antibacterial. All three cycles reach 150 degrees Fahrenheit.

A prolonged hot-water final rinse kills 99.99 percent of the bacteria. Viruses or fungi aren't destroyed. More germs are killed by boiling pleasure toys.

Are toy cleaning sprays effective?

Some writers think sprays are unnecessary and costly, but other writers disagree. Never use cleaning sprays containing parabens, alcohol, petrol, or acetone.[116] Buy a water-based toy cleaner instead. It's handy when traveling. Don't spray the cleaner on genitals, though. Use the spray after sexual activity and relax in bed. Later, rinse the toy.

The Shibari advanced toy spray can be applied to latex, rubber, and silicone. Babeland, a sex shop in New York City, sells LELO's antibacterial toy cleaner. The Daily Dot's recommendations for toy cleaners are 365 Everyday Value fragrance-free hand soap and Clearly Natural Essentials Unscented.

Is a machine available for cleaning pleasure toys?

Spray cleaners or disinfectants are unnecessary when you can use a machine to clean toys. Rinse toys and completely dry them with a clean towel before placing them in a UVee system, a high-tech refractory system. This system uses a UV-C light to kill 99.9 percent of the germs that are found on pleasure toys. The system also sterilizes *E. Coli*, a bacterium that is difficult to destroy.

The UVee Home Play and the UVee GO Play systems simultaneously clean and charge all toys via a USB connection. The systems include a decorated case and a combination lock.

The UVee Home Play, the larger version, has a flexible divider system with space to clean, charge, and store three toys or a large toy such as the Magic Wand Original. Sterilization is complete in ten minutes. The Home Play system has three charging stations with a vacuum-sealed outlet for toys that require an electrical wall outlet. This system costs $180.

The smaller version, the UVee GO Play, stores several compact toys or one standard size vibrator. Pleasure toys are sterilized in five minutes. The UVee GO Play has one charging station and costs $120 at Babeland.

Is a UVee system necessary if toys aren't being shared?

Germs living near the bedroom and bathroom can accumulate on pleasure toys and cause infections. Toys used in solo sex should be cleaned, dried, and stored.

Which materials are used to make vibrators and dildos?

Silicone, ABS hard plastic, and elastomer varieties, including TPR Plastic or thermoplastic rubber, are the materials used to make vibrators. Dildos are produced from silicone, VixSkin

Silicone — a pure silicone simulating real skin — glass, wood, stainless steel, ceramic, natural stone, and Lucite.

Which materials are generally used in harnesses?

Leather, nylon, spandex, and cotton.

Which methods are used to clean nonmotorized, nonporous toys?

You can clean these toys by using hot water with mild soap. Don't use scented hand soap or antibacterial soap because the soap residue can irritate the genitals.

Abrasive products shouldn't be used to clean toys that are made of metal or Lucite. A metal toy that has been boiled retains heat and should be cooled. Gold-plated toys often contain other ingredients and shouldn't be boiled.

Another way to clean toys is to soak silicone, ABS plastic, Pyrex glass, soda-lime glass, metal, Lucite, ceramic, or natural stone in a solution of 90 percent water and 10 percent bleach for 10 minutes.

The third cleaning method involves sterilizing pleasure toys in boiling water for a few minutes. Place a dishtowel in the pot to prevent damage to Pyrex glass. Anal toys should be boiled after every few times of use because silicone retains funky odors.

The fourth cleaning method involves sanitizing toys in the top rack of your dishwasher without using detergents.

How are porous materials cleaned?

Porous materials such as jelly rubber, latex, TPR, TPE, and PVC (polyvinyl chloride) retain bacteria and pathogens. These materials can be sanitized, not sterilized. Clean them with warm water and mild antibacterial soap and dry them vigorously after every use. Wear a polyurethane condom to prevent the transfer of bacteria or STIs including HIV to your partner.

Table 3: Cleaning Methods for Nonmotorized Nonporous Materials

Cleaning Methods	**Silicone**	**ABS Plastic**	**Pyrex glass (Boro-silicate)**	**Glass (soda-lime)**	**Metal (exclude Gold)**
Mild soap & hot water	X	X	X	X	X
Soak in 10 percent bleach and 90 per-cent water solution for 10 minutes.	X	X	X		X
Boiling water for five minutes	X	X	X		X
Dishwasher top rack	X	X	X		X
Alcohol Wipe	X	X			
Toy Cleaner	X	X	X	X	X
Cleaning Methods	**Wood**	**Ceramic**	**Natural Stone**	**Lucite**	
Mild soap & hot water	X	X	X	X	
Soak in 10 percent bleach and 90 per-cent water solution for 10 minutes.		X	X		
Boiling water for five minutes		X	X		
Dishwasher top rack		X	X		
Alcohol Wipe		X			
Toy Cleaner	X	X	X	X	

How can porous realistic materials such as Cyberskin, Pure Skin, Realskin, UR3, and Sensa-Firm be cleaned?

These toys can't be sterilized, but you can clean them with soap and warm water. Don't use too much soap, though. Excessive soap lather can damage the toys, which should be dried well to prevent the growth of mildew.

After being cleaned, porous realistic materials become sticky. So you should sprinkle cornstarch on toys with soft skin to maintain the realistic look and feel. Check before each use for discoloration, new odors, black spots, or evidence of mildew growing in the pores.

Replace toys made with realistic materials every four to six months, and remember that you should never share realistic toys with a partner unless a polyurethane condom is worn.

Table 4: Cleaning Methods for Nonmotorized Porous Materials

Cleaning Methods	TPR thermo-(plastic rubber) TPE (thermo-plastic elastomers)	Jelly Rubber	Latex	PVC (polyvinyl chloride)	Realistic Materials: CyberSkin, Pure Skin, Real Skin, UR3 and Sensa-Firm
Warm water and mild antibacterial soap after each use and dry thoroughly	X	X	X	X	X
Dishwasher's top rack; select sanitize		X		X	X
Toy Cleaner	X	X	X		
Rinse only					X
Sprinkle cornstarch after drying.		X			X
Sharing toys	Wear a polyurethane condom	Wear a polyurethane condom	Wear a polyurethane condom	Wear a polyurethane condom	Wear a polyurethane condom

How should I clean motorized nonporous pleasure toys made from silicone, ABS plastic, Pyrex, glass, and metal?

Remove the batteries before cleaning motorized toys. Electric components should never be submerged in water, boiled, or put in the dishwasher.

Lather soap on a damp cloth to clean motorized toys. Use a fragrance-free, mild antibacterial soap without microbeads or tiny bits of plastic used in exfoliants. Fragrances inflame and irritate the vagina, altering the pH balance of the vulva.

Rinse your motorized toys with hot water. Then dry them with a clean towel to prevent water from damaging them. A solo user who doesn't have a yeast infection or bacterial infection can clean the toys with regular hand soap and water.

Are there specific cleaning instructions for different types of toy materials?

Silicone

Wipe silicone toys with rubbing alcohol before sharing the toys with a partner. These toys will swell afterwards but will then revert to the original form after air drying.

Vixen Creations, a toy company that makes the dual-density VixSkin, successfully tests its material by soaking a silicone vibrator in rubbing alcohol for a day. Dust and fur aren't drawn to the vibrator. Some manufacturers of silky-soft silicone vibrators warn against using this cleaning process.

A vibrator's buttons or battery cover might not be completely covered by silicone. The groove between the silicone and the plastic parts can trap fluid, causing bacterial growth on the surface of the toy.

Use a soft toothbrush to clean cracks in silicone toys.

However, you should avoid using a silicone wash on a silicone toy because the wash can damage the toy. Never use a cleaning process with a chemical ending in cone such as Dimethicone.

ABS Plastic

To clean ABS plastic toys, wipe the toys down or use antibacterial soap and water, mild soap and water, toy cleaner, or rubbing alcohol. Occasionally, the label of a toy will indicate that the toy has a polyurethane coating, which means that rubbing alcohol shouldn't be used for cleaning.

Pyrex and Glass

To clean a Pyrex glass pleasure toy, use soap or bleach and place the toy in boiling water with a small towel to prevent the Pyrex from hitting the side of the pot. Pyrex can be sanitized in the dishwasher without detergent. Don't wash other types of glass toys in the dishwasher because high temperatures can damage them. Instead, wash these toys with soap and water.

Metal

Soak your metal pleasure toy for three minutes in cold water with a 10 percent bleach solution. Then wash the toy with mild soap and water to remove the last vestiges of bleach. Never heat bleach to sanitize metal because it can corrode stainless steel.

Njoy, a sex toy company, manufactures medical-grade stainless steel pleasure toys. The company includes cleaning instructions with its toys.

Wood

Avoid using an abrasive body scrub cleanser or rough cloths to clean wood toys. If you buy a naturally finished wood dildo, don't use a lot of soap to clean it.

Reapply an oil coating after using a wood pleasure toy in the shower every six times to maintain waterproofing.

The manufacturer, NobEssence, produces excellent wood sex toys. Wood can be wiped down with an antibacterial/microbial cleaner such as alcohol, bleach, or peroxide when sharing pleasure toys with partners.

How should motorized pleasure toys be cleaned? Should splash-proof toys or waterproof toys be cleaned differently?

Before washing a pleasure toy, check and secure the base attachment to prevent water from seeping into the DC socket or around the interface.

Avoid washing motorized or vibrating pleasure toys in water because the water might leak inside the toys. You should also read the information on packaging to determine whether your toys are splash-proof or waterproof.

Waterproof toys can be fully submerged in soapy water. Conversely, you can rinse a splash-proof toy under a faucet and then wipe the toy with a lint-free towel cloth.

How should motorized non-waterproof toys be cleaned?

Don't put a non-waterproof vibrating toy or motorized toy in water. Clean the toy with a washcloth, mild soap, and a small amount of water. Then dry the toy with a cloth or paper towel.

Table 5: Cleaning Methods for Motorized Waterproof Toys

Cleaning Methods	Silicone	ABS Plastic	TPR (thermoplastic rubber) TPE (thermoplastic elastomers)	Metal	Skin-Like Realistic Materials
Wipe down with a warm, damp, soapy washcloth and rinse with warm water. Dry with a paper towel.	X	X	X	X	
Rinse only	X	X			X
Toy Cleaner	X	X	X		
Solution consisting of 10 percent bleach and 90 percent water	X	X			
Alcohol Wipe	X	X			

Can TPR and TPE be nonporous?

Nonporous toys made of TPR or TPE are medical-grade version. However, not all are nonporous. Companies such as CalExotics and Doc Johnson claim their TPR toys are nonporous. Ads for pleasure toys can be misleading, so consumers should be careful.

How should I clean Fleshlight's masturbator, the Flight Pilot?

You should purify the Flight Pilot, a toy that's realistic, nontoxic, and porous. The purpose of the purification process is to extract excess residue. After running a lot of water through the sleeve, rinse it several times. Insert one of your fingers in the sleeve to make the cleaning process easier.

To clean the Flight Pilot, rinse the toy with water or use rubbing alcohol. Don't use soap. Dry the Flight Pilot thoroughly. Examine the inside and outside for black spots that are indicative of mildew. Scrub the surface of the toy to remove fungal spores in the pores. An odor is characteristic of mold. Throw the Flight Pilot out if the smell persists.

How should TENGA products be cleaned?

Pleasure toys from TENGA such as the 3D sleeves are combined with antimicrobial silver to protect against bacteria and mold. TENGA's nontoxic, porous Flip Hole toys are most likely made from TPE/TPR. Check for unusual smells and black spots or mildew before cleaning these toys with soap and water.

How should nylon and leather products be cleaned?

Wash nylon harnesses and toys by hand with a mild antibacterial soap or in the washing machine. Never soak leather. However, you should use a damp, soapy cloth or a leather cleaner to wipe down leather products. Then use a leather conditioner afterwards.

Use a 70-percent isopropyl rubbing alcohol solution to wipe down and disinfect leather products containing bodily fluids. Apply a coat of clear nail polish on the metal parts.

How should vinyl products be cleaned?

Wash vinyl toys in warm water only and air dry them. Sprinkle a small amount of cornstarch on the toys to prevent them from becoming sticky.

Should pleasure toys be stored?

Store pleasure toys to prevent bacteria, dust, lint, and pet hair from accumulating on them. A few writers believe that the need to store nonporous toys separately is a myth originating from some manufacturers falsely claiming that their toys were made from silicone. These fake silicone toys were ruined after coming in contact with toys made from other materials. Toys that aren't made of silicone react poorly when stored together. Silicone and shiny ABS plastic toys that touch shouldn't be a problem.

How should pleasure toys be stored?

Cleanse, rinse, and dry your pleasure toys before storing them. Thankfully, many of these toys come in a box, case, or bag, making storage easy. However, you can also buy a partially sheer and washable storage item with a zipper or Velcro if the original package isn't available.

Store porous pleasure toys made from TPR, TPE, PVC, and jelly rubber separately in plastic bags to protect the toys from being damaged. Storing the toys separately prevents them from touching each other and soaking up dyes from each other. Store the toys in a cool, dark place.

Place wooden dildos in a moderately padded satchel to protect the finish from abrasive items. Keep metal, ceramic, and glass toys in a soft cotton drawstring bag.

Avoid keeping toys near oil, powders, and perfumes. Many people put pleasure toys on a nightstand or in an underwear drawer. Store your toy in a pouch when traveling.

How should batteries in pleasure toys be stored?

Remove batteries from pleasure toys that you're not using frequently. Doing so prevents the toys from being damaged by leaking battery acid and corrosion. Don't bother removing the batteries if you're using the toys every day.

Table 6: Cleaning Methods for Nylon, Leather, Metal Parts on Leather, Vinyl, Fleshlight Masturbators, and TENGA Products

Cleaning Methods	Nylon	Leather	Metal Parts on Leather	Vinyl	Fleshlight Masturbators	TENGA products
Washing machine	X					
Wash with mild antibacterial soap and warm water	X					X
Damp, soap cloth		X				
Leather cleaner and leather conditioner		X				
Wipe with 70 percent isopropyl rubbing alcohol solution.		X			X	
Warm water				X		
Air dry				X		
Sprinkle cornstarch				X		
Run water through sleeve, rinse several times, and dry thoroughly.					X	
Apply clear polish.			X			

CHAPTER 10

Pleasure Toys and Relationships

Are you planning to show your partner a favorite pleasure toy? Do you think that your partner might object? How would you address your partner's resistance to pleasure toys? The strategies in this chapter address those concerns and questions.

Research shows that pleasure toys enhance sexual activity and improve sexual health. But some people still have negative beliefs and taboos about pleasure toys.

Do pleasure toys affect baby boomers' sexual satisfaction?

In April 2008, a survey of 1,047 men aged 18 to 60 concluded that men who consistently used vibrators in solo or partner sex scored higher for erectile and orgasmic function, desire, and sexual satisfaction than men who didn't use a pleasure toy.

This study also reported that heterosexual men who used pleasure toys occasionally with partners experienced lower levels of satisfaction than men who never used them. Researchers offer several possible explanations. Many respondents used toys to increase their partners' sexual pleasure. Some respondents thought a vibrator demonstrated a lack of sexual prowess. Some respondents may have exhibited a lower level of sexual satisfaction before using pleasure toys.[117]

A study of gay and bisexual men, and women concluded that they used adult toys more frequently than straight people.[118] Women who have sex with women reported higher levels of satisfaction with a pleasure toy in a 2011 study.[119]

What are some misconceptions about pleasure toys in sex play?

First, the partner might be concerned that he or she may be viewed as a lousy lover. Second, the partner might fear that the pleasure toy will replace him or her.

Third, the partner might feel unsettled by thinking that his or her sex partner will become dependent on pleasure toys for arousal and/or orgasm. Fourth, some individuals might be intimidated by the prospect of buying a pleasure toy.

When is it a good time to talk about bringing pleasure toys into sex play?

There is no perfect time to start a conversation about pleasure toys. It doesn't matter how long partners have been involved before beginning this discussion. Some people want to introduce a pleasure toy immediately. For some individuals, this may be the first time he or she thinks about bringing a toy into sex. Other people don't ask until years later. Some don't desire pleasure toys and never raise the topic.

Where is the best place to have a conversation about pleasure toys?

Before trying something new in sex, partners should have a conversation outside the bedroom. The discussion shouldn't occur before, during, or after having sex. The reason is that heightened emotions affect communication.

Why is it difficult to talk about pleasure toys with a partner?

Recognize that proposing pleasure toys in sex play to a partner is completely normal, although a conversation about it can be difficult. Many people use pleasure toys, but some people are uncomfortable talking about them.

What are the guidelines for discussing pleasure toys with your partner?

Have a conversation, not an argument. Be open and reassuring. Respect your partner's wishes and set boundaries. Don't focus on yourself and your sexual needs. Emphasize the idea that you'll both enjoy pleasure toys.

Why introduce pleasure toys in the bedroom?

Toys are a healthy, enjoyable part of a relationship and bring passion and fun into sex play. Adult toys increase pleasure, sexual satisfaction, and intimacy. These toys are sexual enhancements, like icing on the cake.[120]

Vibrators provide pleasure when applied to the tip of the penis, the perineum, the ball sack, and the vulva. Experimentation with a loving and trustworthy partner is exciting. Exploring one's body with pleasure toys makes it easier for partners to explain to each other what is needed to feel sexually satisfied.

Pleasure toys improve sexual health. Antidepressants and other medications affect sexual desire, arousal, and the ability of men and women to climax. Postmenopausal women who have a low libido and vaginal dryness can orgasm by masturbating with a pleasure toy. A prostate massager provides orgasms more powerful than penile orgasms.

What are some strategies to start talking about pleasure toys with your partner?

Practice asking neutral questions before starting a discussion about pleasure toys. Using such questions can alleviate concerns about being judged by your partner's response. There are several questions that you can ask: *What did you think about the two episodes on Sex and the City when the four women talked about rabbit vibrators and the Hitachi Magic Wand? What are your thoughts on the episode about pegging on Broad Street? What do you think about trying a pleasure toy?*

Straightforward sentences can be effective in beginning a conversation. You can begin a conversation in several ways: *I would really like for us to look at pleasure toys together to intensify sensations for both of us.*

I enjoy having sex with you, and I think it would be fun to bring toys into the bedroom. I would love to try something that you can wear such as a vibrating cock ring.

Some people may be more comfortable sending a text message or writing an email to help jump-start the discussion with a partner. Send an article on older people and pleasure toys. For example, you can send the article, *10 Best Sex Toys for Seniors 2020* (https://mysecretluxury.com/blog/10-best-sex-toys-for-seniors/). Include a note with the article. *I read this article and thought of us. I think it would be exciting to try one of these pleasure toys. I am so interested. Is this something that you think would enhance passion and desire?* [121]

Make it clear that pleasure toys aren't a substitute for another person. Experimentation and experiencing toys together are central to pleasure toys. Watch your partner masturbate with a pleasure toy and you will become aroused and stimulated. A study concluded that both partners reported increased sensations when pleasure toys were part of sex play.[122]

What if your partner isn't open to the idea of using pleasure toys?

Listen to your partner talk about being unwilling to bring pleasure toys into the bedroom. Be positive and respect your partner's wishes. No one should be forced or cajoled into doing something that isn't appealing. Put your sex partner at ease by saying how much enjoyment is received when he or she touches a special spot.[123] Ask your partner about his or her fantasies. This shows that you value your partner's interests.

Resistance to adult toys may be based on misinformation or a previous experience. Refer to Chapter I for myths and facts about pleasure toys.

After agreeing to bring pleasure toys into the bedroom, what's next?

You might have an extensive collection of pleasure toys, but your partner might not feel comfortable using a toy that was shared with previous partners. Buy a new toy to make your partner comfortable.

Set a date to go together to a brick-and-mortar shop or look online to buy a pleasure toy. Babeland, Pleasure Chest, and Good Vibrations are adult sex stores that also have online shops. Share fantasies about which toys are exciting. Each partner may prefer a totally different pleasure toy. Visiting an adult sex store will give you and your partner an opportunity to touch and examine pleasure toys and have salespeople answer your questions. Consider the possibility that your partner might not want to accompany you to an adult sex store.

Another strategy is to begin with a small vibrator to address your partner's concern about being replaced by a pleasure toy. Don't buy a large phallic dildo or a rabbit vibrator with rotating beads. Your partner might think he or she is being replaced by a dildo or vibrator. Choose a pleasure toy that is quiet and doesn't look like a toy. Buy something that's more adorable than sexual. The Bender pleasure toy from Unbound looks like Gumby, and the Form II from Jimmyjane looks like a bunny.

Consider the Fin, a Dame product that is one of the best toys for beginners. This pleasure toy can be placed between your fingers. The Fin is held in place with a strap and becomes a vibrator. Vibrators that can be enjoyed by two people include Touch by We-Vibe, the Lovehoney Desire Remote Control Love Egg vibrator, and the Eva II by Dame Products. View Appendix F in this book for a list of pleasure toys.

When bringing a pleasure toy into sex play, make it part of the experience and not the entire focus. Avoid mentioning the toy.

Guide your partner's hand to spots that bring intense pleasure. Tell your partner how sexy he or she is and say that you love your partner's penis, vulva, or body. Verbal encouragement or dirty talk adds to the excitement.

Can a relationship be ruined if one partner refuses to accept toys as part of sex play?

A partner who opposes pleasure toys in sexual activity might be rigid about experimentation or just not interested. Decide whether pleasure toys are an absolute must in the relationship.

Solo masturbation with a pleasure toy to reach orgasm works when you have an unwilling partner.

How do satisfied people describe their sexual relationship?

Partners make an effort to prevent sex from becoming routine and boring. Adults who are satisfied report passion, playfulness, cuddling, and laughing. They talk about fantasies and role-play them, light candles, and play music to create an exciting and romantic mood.

Lovers report trying out a new sexual position, engage in oral sex, wear sexy lingerie, bathe or shower together, use pleasure toys, give each other massages, go on romantic getaways, and plan a date night to have sex. Openness about pleasure toys and acceptance by a partner enhances sexual satisfaction. Most important is the ability to communicate your love to each other.[124]

APPENDIX A

Sex-Positive Retail Adult Sex Stores for Feminists, Couples, and the LGBTQIAP+ Community

The Center for Sexual Pleasure and Health[125] and Adult Video News (AVN)[126] recommended these retail adult sex shops. Call before you go to confirm that it is open for business. Check the website for social distance guidelines.

California

Good Vibrations is known as the premier sex-positive retailer that provides erotic body-safe sex toys, books, movies, and quality erotica products.
Website: www.goodvibes.com
Address: 603 Valencia St. at 17th, San Francisco, CA 94110
Phone: (415) 503-9522

Mr. S Leather in business since 1979 is the largest and best selection of BDSM, kink gear, sex toys, anal play, bondage restraints and hoods, leather harnesses, and more. Hankey's Toys and

SquarePeg Toys who make extra small to extra-large dildos are sold in this adult sex shop
Website: www.mr-s-leather.com
Address: 385 8th St., San Francisco, SoMa, CA 94103
Phone: (800)746-7677

Rock Hard originally opened in 1998 as an erotic art store. In 1999, it began selling more erotica, lotions, sex toys, DVD videos, and novelties. It is gay-friendly and is located in the heart of the Castro District.
Website: https://rockhardsf.business.site
Address: 518 Castro St., Between 19th & 18th STS,
San Francisco, CA 94114
Phone: (415) 437-2430

Illinois

Early to Bed has book clubs and other events to provide feminist and queer communities to meet each other. Currently, hours are restricted due to Covid-19. Check website for more information.
Website: early2bed.com
Address: 5044 N Clark St., Chicago, IL 60640
Phone: (773) 271-1219

Hustler Hollywood is located in a lovely outdoor shopping mall at North Avenue and Clybourne with a great selection of clothing, costumes, sex toys, kink gear, lingerie, and personal lubricants.
Website: www.hustlerhollywood.com
Address: 1615 N Clybourn Ave., Chicago, IL 60614
Phone: (312) 846-6520

The Pleasure Chest believes that everyone has a basic right to pursue sexual fulfillment. Currently offers virtual workshops

on Instagram. Check @pleasurecheststores for upcoming workshops filmed live and saved for future viewing on the stores IGTV official site of Instagram.
Website: www.thepleasurechest.com
Address: 1448 N Milwaukee Ave., Chicago, IL 60622
Phone: (773) 525-7151

New York State

New York City

Upper East Side

The Pleasure Chest spans 6,000 square feet and is the largest erotic boutique in Manhattan. This shop offers free virtual sex workshops. Shop for vibrators, dildos, strap-ons, anal toys, kink, pleasure toys for couples, and men, sexual health products, sexual enhancers and pleasure, teasing and massage toys, gender affirmation products, and books.
Website: www.thepleasurechest.com
Address: 1150 2nd Ave., New York, NY 10065
Phone: (212) 355-6909

West Village

The Pleasure Chest opened in 1971 and was the first erotic sex toy shop to create a boutique atmosphere.
Website: www.thepleasurechest.com
Address: 156 7th Ave S., New York, NY 10014
Phone: (212) 242-2158

Bronx

Romantic Depot Bronx Sex Store, Sex Shop & Lingerie Store is the largest adult store and lingerie shop in the NYC tri-state area and in northeastern U.S. With over 10,000 square feet it offers every major brand of vibrators, adult toys, sexy lingerie

for women and men of all orientations, gifts for parties, funny gags, adult board games, BDSM (bondage and discipline, domination and submission, sadism and masochism) toys, bondage gear, personal lubricants, nipple clamps, dildos, anal toys, couple toys, blow-up dolls, edible erotic toys, condoms, and much more.
Website: www.romanticdepot.com
Address: 3703 Provost Ave., Bronx, NY 10466
Phone: (718) 515-6969

Manhattan
Romantic Depot Manhattan Sex Store Sex Shop & Lingerie Store stocks large selections of pleasure toys for gay men.
Website: www.romanticdepot.com
Address: 3418 Broadway, NYC, NY 10031
Phone: (646) 861-0683

Queens
Romantic Depot Queens Sex Store, Sex Shop & Lingerie Store reopened on Queens Boulevard on June 23, 2021—two years after its former Sunnyside store burned to the ground in a massive fire. This store sells racy lingerie in a range of sizes as well as edible underwear, penis enlargement cream, and adult toys for bachelorette parties. Also sold are strap-ons, dildos, harnesses, nipple rings and vibrators which are on display in a cordoned off section of the store—behind a red velvet curtain and not visible from the street. The staff posses a non-judgmental attitude, providing a sex positive atmosphere, sexual wellness, and a 100% inclusive environment.
Website: www.romanicdepot.com
Address: 47-02 Queens Blvd, Queens, NY 11104
Phone: (914) 689-1238

Rockland County
Romantic Depot Rockland Sex Store & Lingerie Shop has a sex-positive reputation. High-quality pleasure products and education on the correct and safe use of sex toys is available.
Website: www.romanticdepot.com
Address: 301 Route 59, East St., West Nyack, NY 10994
Phone: (845) 353-0180

Yonkers
Romantic Depot Yonkers Sex Store, Sex Shop & Lingerie is a super lingerie store. About 80% of its floor space has non-adult product lines in a mainstream, safe, and elegant setting. Besides all types of sexy lingerie and sizes, a customer can find couples games, romantic gifts, flavored lubricants, gag gifts, and dance-wear. This sex shop stocks vibrators, pleasure toys, BDSM toys, fetish toys, strap-ons, marital aids and other adult products. Batteries are tested before purchase. A 20% discount is given to military, firefighter, law enforcement, and EMS workers.
Website: www.romanticdepot.com
Address: 1937 Central Park Ave., Yonkers, NY 10710
Phone: (914) 787-8788

Maryland
Sugar, an adult sex shop provides education and pleasure toys in a shame free, sex positive, and fun environment with the goal of people of all genders and sexual orientations experiencing sexuality with passion and joy. This sex shop is lesbian owned and operated by multi-gender people.
Website: www.sugartheshop.com
Address: 1001 W. 36th St, Baltimore, MD 21211
Phone: (410) 467-2632

Minnesota

The Smitten Kitten is a progressive sex toy shop for people of all genders and orientations.
Website: Smittenkittenonline.com
Address: 3010 Lyndale Ave S., Minneapolis, MN 55408
Phone: (612) 721-6088

Wisconsin

Tool Shed Toys is Milwaukee's only mission-driven pleasure toy store that sells quality, non-toxic body-safe toys, and gifts for people of all genders and sexual orientations.
Website: www.toolshedtoys.com
Address: 2427 N. Murray Ave., 53211 Milwaukee, WI
Phone: (414) 906-5304

APPENDIX B

Brick-and-Mortar Sex Shops Sell Extra Small to Giant Size Dildos

Hankey's Toys, SquarePeg Toys, and Self Serve are manufacturers of extra small to giant size dildos. Their products can be found in the adult sex stores listed below. Call before you visit to confirm that the sex shop is open for business. Check their website for social distance guidelines.

Hankey's Toys are sold at these stores

California
Mr. S Leather
Website: www.mr-s-leather.com
Address: 385 8th St., San Francisco, SoMa, CA 94103
Phone: (800) 746-7677

Gear Leather & Fetish
Website: www.gearleather.com
Address: 650 E Sunny Dunes Rd#1, Palm Springs, CA 92264
Phone: (760) 322-3363

Pleasures and Treasures
Website: https://pandtstore.com
Address: 2525 University Ave., San Diego, CA 92104
Phone: (619) 822-4280

New York City
The Leather Man
Website: www.theleatherman.com
Address: 111 Christopher St., New York, NY 10014
Phone: (212) 243-5339

SquarePeg Toys are sold at these stores

California
Gear Leather & Fetish
Website: www.gearleather.com
Address: 650 E Sunny Dunes, Palm Springs, CA 92264
Phone: (760) 322-3363

Mr S Leather
Website: www.mr-s-leather.com
Address: 385 8th St., San Francisco, CA 94103
Phone: (800) 746-7677

Pleasures and Treasures
Website: https://pandtstore.com
Address: 2525 University Ave., San Diego, CA 92104
Phone: (619) 822-4380

Florida
LeatherWerks
Website: https://secure.leatherwerks.com

Address: 126 NE 4th Ave., Fort Lauderdale, FL 33304
Phone: (954) 761-1236

Illinois

Full Kit Gear
Website: https://hub.fetish-x.com/sexshop/full-kit-gear-90
Address: 5021 N. Clark St., Chicago, IL 60640
Phone: (773) 657-8000

Massachusetts

Full Kit Gear
Website: https://hub.fetish-x.com/sexshop/full-kit-gear-90
Address: 192 Commercial St., Provincetown, MA 02657
Phone: (508) 413-9676

New Jersey

PeepShow Toys
Online Store
Website: https://www.peepshowtoys.com
Phone: (551) 225-1424

New York

SheVibe
Online Retailer
Website: https://shevibe.com
Phone: (888) 743-8423

The Leather Man
Website: www.theleatherman.com
Address: 111 Christopher St., New York, NY 10014
Phone: (212) 243-5339

Washington

Doghouse Leathers
Website: www.doghouseleathers.com
Address: 715 E Pine St., Seattle, WA 98122
Phone: (206) 257-0231

Wisconsin

Tool Shed Toys
Website: https://www.toolshedtoys.com
Address: 2427 N. Murray Ave., Milwaukee, WI 53211
Phone: (414) 906-5304

Self Serve Toys are sold at these stores

New Mexico

Self Serve Sexuality Resource Center
Website: www.selfservetoys.com
Address: 112 Morningside Dr NE., Albuquerque, NM 87108
Phone: (505) 265-5815

APPENDIX C

Retail Adult Stores Sell Body-Safe Pleasure Toys

The Center of Sexual Pleasure and Health located in Providence, Rhode Island recommended these brick-and mortar-shops to purchase pleasure toys.[127] The majority of these reputable adult sex stores are run and owned by feminists and can be found all over the United States and in Canada. The retailers who closed their sex shops during the Pandemic of 2020 are indicated. Call the adult sex shop before you visit to confirm that it is open for business. Check the website for social distance guidelines.

Arizona

Fascinations sells lingerie, sex toys, bondage toys, and personal lubricants.
Website: https://www.fascinations.net
Address: 5930 W. Greenway Rd., Glendale, AZ 85306. Located in Greenway Promenade
Phone: (602) 843-0577
Address: 16428 N 32nd St., Phoenix, AZ 85032

Phone: (602) 482-3633
Address: 838 W Elliot Rd., Tempe, AZ 85284
Phone: (480) 222-0040
Address: 3658 E Speedway Blvd., Tucson, AZ 85716
Phone: (520) 322-0757

California

Good Vibrations is known as a premier sex-positive retailer that provides body-safe sex toys, books, videos, and quality erotica products.
Website: goodvibes.com
Address: 899 Mission St., San Francisco, CA 94103. Located in Yerba Buena Shops
Phone: (415) 513-163
Address: 603 Valencia St. at 17th St. San Francisco, CA 94110
Phone: (415) 503-9522
Address: 1620 Polk St., San Francisco, CA 94109.
Phone: (415) 345-0400
Address: 2504 San Pablo Ave. Berkeley, CA 94702
Phone: (510) 841-8987

Mr. S Leather specializes in bondage, BDSM, anal play, sex toys, leather, and rubber pleasure.
Website: www.mr-s-leather.com
Address: 385 8th St. San Francisco, SoMa, CA 94103
Phone: (800) 746-7677

Trystology is a women-owned business that sells quality sensual lingerie (sizes from 32A to 40E) from Europe and the U.S., quality sex toys, and personal lubricants.
Website: Trystology.com
Address: 588 E. Main Street, Ventura, CA 93001
Phone: (888) 801- 8952

FeelMore 510 sells quality toys and condoms
Website: https://feelmore510.com
Address: 703 Telegraph Ave., Oakland, CA 94612
Phone: (510) 891-0199

Pure Pleasure in Santa Cruz, CA — Reported closed

The Rubber Rose, San Diego, CA — Permanently Closed

Colorado

Fascinations: focuses on lingerie, sex toys, bondage toys, and personal lubricants. This shop has two floors making available a very large collection of pleasure toys.
Website: www.fascinations.net
Address: 4111 E Virginia Ave., Glendale, CO 80246
Phone: (303) 322-3324
Address: 1752 Dublin Blvd., Colorado Springs, CO 80918
Phone: (719) 694-2865
Address: 5177 W 64th Ave., Arvada, CO 80003
Phone: (303) 412-1128
Address: 2680 S Havana St., Aurora, CO 80014
Phone: (303) 750-5200
Address: 10550 W Colfax Ave., Lakewood, CO 80215
Phone: (303) 202-1855

Illinois

Early to Bed has book clubs and other events to provide feminist and queer communities to meet each other. Currently, hours are restricted due to Covid-19. Check website for more information.
Website: early2bed.com
Address: 5044 N Clark St., Chicago, IL 60640
Phone: (773) 271-1219

Maine

Nomia Boutique is the first women owned and operated sexuality boutique in Northern New England. It has a large selection of sex products and good prices for books, body-safe sex toys, and personal lubricants.
Website: nomiaboutique.com
Address: 24 Exchange St STE 215, Portland, Maine 04101
Phone: (207) 773-4774

Maryland

Sugar, an adult sex shop provides education and pleasure toys in a shame free, sex positive, and fun environment with the goal of people of all genders and sexual orientations experiencing their sexuality with passion and joy. This sex shop is lesbian owned and operated by multi-gender people.
Website: www.sugartheshop.com
Address: 1001 West 36th St., Baltimore, MD 21211
Phone: (410) 467-2632

Massachusetts

Good Vibrations is known as a premier sex-positive retailer that provides body-safe sex toys, books, videos, and quality erotica products.
Website: www.goodvibes.com
Address: 308 Harvard St. A, Brookline, MA 6 02446
Phone: (617) 487-4990

Oh My Sensuality Shop is owned by a mother and daughter team who promote a pleasure positive perspective that everyone has the right to express their own unique sensuality. Classes, events, high quality toys, books, condoms, and personal lubricants are available.
Website: www.ohmysensuality.com
Address: 122 Main St., Northhampton, MA 01060
Phone: (413) 584-9669

Minnesota

The Smitten Kitten is a progressive sex toy shop for people of all genders and orientations.
Website: Smittenkittenonline.com
Address: 3010 Lyndale Ave S., Minneapolis, MN 55408
Phone: (612) 721-6088

New Mexico

Self Serve Sexuality Resource Center focuses on health and education.
Website: selfservetoys.com
Address: 112 Morningside Dr NE., Albuquerque, NM 87108
Phone: (505) 265-5815

New York City

Babeland is a women-friendly sex toy retailer
Website: https://www.babeland.com
Address: 43 Mercer St., New York, NY 10013
Phone: (212) 966-2120
Address: 94 Rivington St., New York, NY 10002
Phone: (212) 375-1701

New York State

Sustainable Passions emphasizes health and safety
Website: https://sustainablepassions.com
Address: 311 N Meadow St., Ithaca, NY14850
Phone: (607) 280-5950

Oregon

Fascinations — reported closed.

She Bop is a women-owned sex toy shop specializing in body-safe products and education.
Website: shebopttheshop.com
Address: 3213 SE Division St., Portland, OR 97202
Phone: (503) 688-1196

Pennsylvania

PASSIONAL Boutique combined with Sexploratorium in 2007 to offer more sex products. PASSIONAL Boutique sells corsets, kilts, costumes, traditional fetishware (leather and latex) for all body types and all genders, and high fashion theatrical wardrobes in sizes XXS-8XL. Its partner store, Sexploratorium offers body-safe, guaranteed-quality sexuality products, sexuality education classes, and resources. Because of the pandemic only online shopping and online classes are available.
Website: https://passionalboutique.com
Address: 317 South St., Philadelphia, PA 19147
Phone: (215) 829-4986

Wisconsin

A Woman's Touch in Wisconsin, a sex education resource center and sexual health products store is managed by two women, a physician, a sex educator and counselor that provide information and pleasure products. Products for sex after menopause are also for sale. Transgender, cisgender, and non-binary people are welcome.[140]
Website: https://sexualityresources.com
Address: 302 S. Livingston St., Madison, WI 53703
Phone: (608) 250-1928

Tool Shed Toys is Milwaukee's only mission-driven pleasure toy store that sells quality, non-toxic body-safe toys and gifts for people of all genders and sexual orientations.
Website: www.toolshedtoys.com
Address: 2427 N. Murray Ave., 53211 Milwaukee, WI
Phone: (414) 906-5304

Canada

Come As You Are is a worker-owned cooperative providing a safe and comfortable environment for accessing sex information, sex products, and making pleasure toys accessible to people with disabilities.
Website: comeasyouare.com
Address: 254 Augusta Ave., Toronto, ON MST 2L7, CA
Phone: +1 (416) 504-7934

Good For Her is temporarily closed for in-store shopping. Now offering video shopping appointments. Online store is open and offers curbside pickups. Before the pandemic, Good For Her had workshops on orgasm techniques, burlesque, bondage, and more. A separate section on gender expression is available. On Sundays, from noon to 2:00PM, shopping is reserved only for women and trans to make them feel comfortable.
Website: https:// goodforher.com
Address: 175 Harbord St.,Toronto, ON M5S iH3, CA
Phone: +1 (416) 588-0900

Trinity Romance in Squamish, BC, CA. Permanently closed

Womyns'Ware is a sex positive shop that focuses on women's sexual health. This adult store has books, vibrators, dildos, lubricants, bondage gear, S/M toys, jewelry, menstrual products, and contraceptive and sexually transmitted infections (STIs) protection. Men are welcome in this adult sex shop.
Website: https://womynsware.com
Address: 896 Commercial Dr., Vancouver, BC V5L 3Y5, CA
Phone:+1 (604)-254-2543

APPENDIX D

Manufacturers of Body-Safe and Sex-Positive Pleasure Toys

The Center for Sexual Pleasure and Health recommended these sex-toy manufacturers.[128]

Aneros	www.aneros.com
BMS Factory	https://www.bmsfactory.com
Crystal Delights	https://crystaldelights.com
Divine Interventions	https://so-divine.com
Fun Factory.	https://us.funfactory.com
Happy Valley	http://happyvalleysilicone.com
Je Joue	https://www.jejoue.com
Jimmyjane	https://jimmyjane.com
Laid	www.laidproducts.com
OhMiBod	ohmibod.com
Tantus	https://www.tantusinc.com
Tenga	https://usstore.tenga.co/
Vibratex	https://vibratex.com
Vixen Creations	https://vixen-creations.myshopify.com
Wet for Her	https://www.wetforher.com
We-Vibe	https://www.we-vibe.com/us/

APPENDIX E

Brand Names of Lubricants, Manufacturers, and pH and Osmolality Levels

Data in Table 1: World Health Organization (2012) in collaboration with United Nations Population Fund (UNFPA) and Family Health International (FH1360) evaluated personal lubricants.[129] The World Health Organization (WHO) recommends using a personal lubricant with a pH of 4.5 and an osmolality below 1200 mOsm/kg. A rectal lubricant's pH level should range from 5.5 to 7.

Table 7: World Health Organization's Evaluation of Personal Lubricants

Lubricant	Manufacturer	Osmolality	pH
KY Jelly	Johnson & Johnson Langhorne, PA, USA	2007	4.55
KY Warming Jelly	Johnson & Johnson Langhorne PA, USA	ND	4.50- 6.50

Lubricant	Manufacturer	Osmolality	pH
KY Tingling Jelly	Johnson & Johnson Langhorne, PA, USA	5047	3.61
KY Sensual Silk	Johnson & Johnson Langhorne, PA, USA	5467	3.39
KY Sensual Silk Warming	Johnson & Johnson Langhorne, PA, USA	ND	5.00-7.00
KY Sensual Silk Tingling Ultragel	Johnson & Johnson Langhorne, PA, USA	5381	3.36
KY Natural Feeling Liquid	Johnson & Johnson Langhorne, PA, USA	4523	3.86
Wet Original Gel Lubricant	Trigg Laboratories Valencia, PA, USA	3679	5.9
Wet Light	Trigg Laboratories Valencia, PA, USA	3946	6.02
Wet Warming	Trigg Laboratories Valencia, PA, USA	ND	6.0-7.5
Durex Play Soothing	Ssl international London, United Kingdom	1373	4.2
Durex Play Warmer	Ssl international London, United Kingdom	ND	4
Durex Play Pina Colada	Ssl international London, United Kingdom	ND	4.29
Durex Play More	Ssl international London, United Kingdom	1332	4.49
ID Glide	Westridge Laboratories Inc. Santa Ana, CA, USA	2901	5.2
ID Juicy Lube Cherry	Westridge Laboratories Inc. Santa Ana, CA, USA	3030	5.35

Brand Names of Lubricants, Manufacturers, and pH and Osmolality Levels

Lubricant	Manufacturer	Osmolality	pH
ID Pleasure	Westridge Laboratories Inc. Santa Ana, CA, USA	2898	5.26
ID Sensation	Westridge Laboratories Inc. Santa Ana, CA, USA	ND	5.95-6.6
Astroglide Liquid	BioFilm Inc. Vista CA, USA	8064	4.44
Astroglide Gel	BioFilm Inc Vista, CA, USA	2299	4.3
Astroglide Warming Liquid	BioFilm Inc. Vista, CA, USA	ND	6.45-6.73
Astroglide Glycerin & Paraben-Free Liquid	BioFilm Inc. Vista, CA, USA	4806	4.54
Astroglide Strawberry	BioFilm Inc Vista, CA, USA	ND	5.35
Astroglide Silken Secret	BioFilm Inc. Vista, CA, USA	6121	4.73
Lifestyles Liquid (with Aloe & Vit. E)	Ansell Limited Richmond, Victoria, Australia	4229	6.3
Lifestyles Excite Sensual Gel	Ansell Limited Richmond, Victoria, Australia	3728	7.2
Lifestyles Warm Lovin'	Ansell Limited Richmond, Victoria, Australia	ND	5.24
Maximus	Bodywise Limited Isle of Wight, United Kingdom	6415	6.05

Lubricant	Manufacturer	Osmolality	pH
Babelube	Babeland Seattle, WA, USA	19	6.78
Elbow Grease Thin Gel	B. Cumming Company Sun Valley, CA, USA	2977	5.77
Slippery Stuff Gel	Wallace O'Farrell Inc. Puyallup, WA, USA	13	6.89
O' My Natural Lubricant	O' My Products Inc. Vancouver, BC. Canada	4348	5.46
Liquid Silk	Bodywise Limited Isle of Wight, United Kingdom	3167	5.26
Probe Personal Lubricant	Darvryan Laboratories Inc. Portland, OR, USA	341	7.67
Anal Lube Original Formula	California Exotic Novelties Inc. Chino, CA, USA	3456	5.77
ForPlay Gel-Plus	Trimensa Pharmaceuticals Newbury Park, CA, USA	9177	6.58
Gua Oil H20	Empowered Products Inc. Newbury Park, CA, USA	3955	5.61
Duane Reade Lubricating Jelly	Duane Reade Inc. New York, NY, USA	737	4.79
Moist again Vaginal Moisturizing Gel	Lake Consumer Products Inc. Jackson, WI, USA	187	5.68
Replens	Lil' Drug Store Products Inc. Cedar Rapids, IA, USA	1491	2.98
Fem Glide	Cooper Surgical Inc. Puyallup, WA, USA	15	6.13

Data in Table 2 is a range of scores. The mean is indicated below the range scores. For comparison purposes, a gel corresponding to the Universal Placebo was also included in this study.[130] The Universal gel was prepared according to a previously described formula by dissolving HEC (2.7 g) in water (96.3 g) containing sodium chloride (0.85 g) and sorbic acid (0.1 g). The final pH was adjusted to 4.4 by adding sodium hydroxide, and the gel was stored at 2–8 C.

Table 8: Safety of Commercially Available Vaginal Lubricants

Product	pH-Range and Mean Scores	Osmolality-Range & Mean Scores	Manufacturers
Fillergyn	4.4-4.6 4.5. Mean	985-997 991	BSDpharma Lodi, Italy
Geliofil Classic	3.7-3.9 3.8 Mean	3571-3593 3,582	Laboratoires Effik, Meudon-la-Forêt, France
GelSea gel	5.6-5.8 5.7 Mean	3,781-3813 3,797	LDPSA Paris, France
Ginix gel	4.9-5.1 5.0. Mean	980-998 989	ISUS Lisbon, Portugal
Ginix Plus gel	4.9-5.1 5.0. Mean	969-985 977	ISUS, Lisbon, Portugal
Hyalo Gyn	4.7-4.9 4.8 Mean	1,329-1343 1336	Fidia Farmaceutici Abano Terme, Italy
K-Y Jelly	3.4-3.6 3.5 Mean	3,348-3374 3,361	Johnson & Johnson Issy les Moulineaux, France

Product	pH-Range and Mean Scores	Osmolality-Range & Mean Scores	Manufacturers
Phyto Soya gel	4.5-4.7 4.6. Mean	1,220-1232 1,226	Arkopharma Laboratoires Pharmaceutiques, Carros, France
RepHresh gel	2.9-3.1 3.0 Mean	1,433-1445 1,439	Lil' Drug Store Products, Cedar Rapids, IA, USA
Replens gel	2.9-3.1 3.0. Mean	1,172-1182 1,177	Lil' Drug Store Products Cedar Rapids IA, USA
Velastisa Intim VG moisturizer gel cream	3.6-3.8 3.7. Mean	1,144-1158 1,151	Isdin Barcelona, Spain
Vidermina gel	4.8-5.0 4.9. Mean	3,691-3723 3,707	Istituto Ganassini, Milano, Italy
Universal Placebo	4.3-4.5 4.4. Mean	296-300 298	

Table 9: Evaluation of Over-the-Counter Personal Lubricants for Safety and Anti-HIV-1 Activity.[131]

Lubricant	Osmolality	pH	Manufacturers
Astroglide	6113	4.0	BioFilm. Inc. Vista, CA, USA
Elbow Grease	3865	5.7	B. Cumming Company Sun Valley, CA, USA
Good Clean Love	269	4.8	Good Clean Love, Inc. Eugene, Oregon, USA
Gynol H	1406	4.7	Caldwell Consumer Health, LLC Parsippany, NJ, USA
ID Glide Ultra long-lasting	3150	5.2	Westridge Laboratories, Inc. Santa Ana, CA.
KY Jelly	2510	4.5	Johnson & Johnson Issy les, Moulineaux, France
PRE Seed	502	7.3	Church & Dwight Co., Inc. Princeton, NJ, USA
Replens	1875	2.9	Lil' Drug Store Products, Cedar Rapids, IA, USA
Slippery Stuff	26	6.5	Wallace O'Farrell, Inc. Puyallup, WA
Sliquid Organic	106	6.8	Sliquid, Inc. Dallas, Texas
Boy butter H2O	1307	7.4	Boy Butter NYC, NY
Boy Butter original	NA	NA	Boy Butter NYC, NY
FC 2 lubricant	NA	NA	Kitchener Ontario, Canada
Wet Platinum	NA	NA	Trigg Laboratories Valencia, CA

APPENDIX F

Pleasure Toys for Baby Boomers

Women

Fiera Arouser
Magic Wand Original
Palm Power Massager
LELO Smart Wand
Rose Kegel Exercise Vaginal Weights
Eroscillator
Eva 2
Vibrating Dilators

Men

Je Joue Mio Vibrating Ring
Pulse Solo
Pulse Duo
Fleshlight Flight Pilot
Simple Pleasure Prostate Massager
Palqueth 3
Hugo™

Partners

Magic Wand Original
Eroscillator Golden Spoon attachments
Je Joue Mio Vibrating Ring Pulse Duo
Rabbit vibrators
Eva 2
Mystery Vibe Crescendo
We-Vibe Melt
Liberator Wedge

Pleasure Toys and Relationships

Bender from Unbound
Form II from JimmyJane
Vibrating Ring
Vibrating Harness
The Fin from Dame Products

End Notes

1. Comella, 2018.
2. Herbenick et al, 2009, Section Results, para 2.
3. Herbenick et al, 2009, Section Results, para 5.
4. National Survey of Sexual Health and Behavior, 2010.
5. Kunst, 2019.
6. Reece et al., 2010, Section, Results, p.1869, para 3.
7. Herbenick, Reece, Sanders, Dodge, Ghassemi, & Fortenbery, 2010.
8. Laumann, Paik & Rosen, 1999, Table 1, Results, p. 539.
9. McBride and Fortenberry, 2010, p.127, para 3.
10. DiDomizio, 2015.
11. Lloyd, 2005, p.27.
12. Stabile, 2013, p.173.
13. Chen, 2020, paras 22, 23, 24, and 25.
14. Burns, 2016. Section: How has the business of adult novelties progressed over the years, and where do you see the industry heading? para 2.
15. Grand View Research, 2021, para 1.
16. Lieberman, 2017, p. 287.
17. BBC Radio 4 in Four, 2018.
18. Ryder, 2013.
19. Vargas-Cooper, 2013.
20. Blue, 2008.
21. Comella, 2017.

22. Rawls, 2007.
23. CBS News, 2010.
24. Rawls, 2007.
25. Comella, 2017.
26. Herbenick, Reece, Sanders, Dodge, Ghassemi, & Fortenbery, 2010.
27. Herbenick et al., 2010, Section: Results: Vibrator Use and Health, para 3.
28. Lloyd, 2006, pp.36-37.
29. Herbenick et al., 2010, Section:Discussion, para 3.
30. Herbenick et al., 2009, Section: Conclusion, para 1.
31. Silver, 2015.
32. Gottlieb, 2004.
33. Leitzmann, Platz, Stampler, Willett & Giovannucci, 2004.
34. Garnick, ed., 2017.
35. Sperling, 2014.
36. Gum, 2019, blog.
37. Gum, 2019, blog.
38. Gum, 2019, blog.
39. Thorn, 2020.
40. Gunter, 2020.
41. Maragakis, 2020.
42. Gunter, 2020.
43. Gunter, 2020.
44. Gunter, 2020.
45. Gunter, 2020.
46. Gunter, 2020.
47. Lieberman, 2017.
48. Comella, 2018.
49. DangerousLilly, 2015, blog.
50. Languist, 2020.
51. Dr. Barb DePree, 2013.

52. Dr. Barb DePree, 2013.
53. Chatel, 2018, para 1.
54. Bendix, 2018, para 1.
55. Bendix, 2018, para 2.
56. Chatel, 2018, para 1.
57. Bendix, 2018, para 2.
58. Bendix, 2018, para 3.
59. Bendix, 2018, para 4.
60. Bendix, 2018, para 5.
61. Chatel, 2018.
62. Chatel, 2018.
63. Chatel, 2018, para 10.
64. Chatel, 2018.
65. Felicity, 2020.
66. LELO, 2015.
67. LELO, 2015.
68. Gurley, 2015.
69. Frank, 2014, para 7.
70. Frank, 2014, para 6 & 7.
71. Reid, 2019, para 11.
72. Silicone Wives.
73. Gurley, 2015, para 32.
74. Frank, 2014, para 5 & 6.
75. Frank, 2014, para 5 & 6.
76. Stubbs, 1993.
77. Brenoff, 2016.
78. DangerousLilly, 2015, blog.
79. Ersner-Hershfield & Kopel, 1979.
80. Goldman, 2003.
81. National Council on Aging, n.d.
82. Lieberman & Cuadrado, 2005.
83. Street, 2009.

84. Glickman, 2015.
85. Silver, 2015.
86. GVibe, 2017, blog.
87. Ruby, 2015, blog.
88. United States Consumer Product Safety Commission, 2018.
89. Melancon, 2019.
90. Hochberger, 2016.
91. Ruby, 2015, blog.
92. Hochberger, 2016.
93. Ruby, 2015, blog.
94. Hochberger, 2019- 4 questions…article.
95. Brabaw, 2018.
96. Ruby, 2015. Blog.
97. Grand View Research, 2019, para 2.
98. Grand View Research, 2019, para 1.
99. Herbenick et al., 2014, p.645, Results, para 3.
100. Reece et al., 2014, Results, Lubricant use, History, p.1128, para 3.
101. Dodge et al., 2014, Results, p.2399, Table I, para 2.
102. WHO, 2012, Safety Issues, para 4 & 5.
103. Dezzutti et al., 2014.
104. Dezzutti et al., 2014.
105. Herbenick et al., 2011.
106. Jozkowski et al., 2013.
107. Edwards & Panay, 2016.
108. Gorbach et al., 2012.
109. Brown et al., 2013, Results, para 7.
110. WHO, 2012, Table I.
111. Hart, #1 Guide to Sex Lubes, 2019, blog.
112. Hess, 2015.
113. Lanquist, 2018.
114. Anderson et al., 2014.

115. Steig, Jan 26, 2018, blog, based on interview with Claire Cavanah, co-founder of Babeland, a sex shop in New York City.
116. Steig, 2018, blog.
117. Reece et al., 2009.
118. Reece et al., 2009.
119. Schick, Herbenick, Rosenberger& Reece, 2011.
120. Kassel, 2019.
121. Kassel, 2019.
122. Kassel, 2019.
123. Smith, 2018.
124. Frederick, Lever, Gillespie, & Garcia, 2017.
125. Center for Sexual Pleasure & Health, 2020.
126. Speiser, 2020.
127. Center for Sexual Pleasure & Health, 2020.
128. Center for Sexual Pleasure and Health, 2020.
129. World Health Organization (2012) in collaboration with United Nations Population Fund (UNFPA) and Family Health International (FH1360), Advisory note.
130. Cunha et al., 2014.
131. Dezzutti et al., 2012.

References

Anderson, T.A., Schick, A., Herbenick D., Dodge, B., & Fortenberry, J.D. A study of human papillomavirus on vaginally inserted sex toys, before and after cleaning, among women who have sex with women and men. *Sexually Transmitted Infections* 2014; 90: 529-531. doi.org/10.1136/sextrans-2014-051558

BBC Radio 4 in Four. (2018, September 9). *Nine Facts that shed light on the big business of sex toys.* Retrieved from https://www.bbc.co.uk/programmes/articles/5210wQsVlRdsbB38lyLQ8xh/nine-facts-that-shed-light-on-the-big-business-of-sex-toys

Bendix, T. (2018, May 11). *Three out of Four Americans have Dildos.* Intomore. Retrieved from https://www.intomore.com/

Blue, V. (2008, November 20). *MacLife review: The OhMiBod* [Web log post]. Retrieved from https://www.tinynibbles.com/

Brabaw, K. (2018, May 11). *How to Know that your Sex Toy is Safe.* Refinery29. Retrieved from https://www.refinery29.com/

Brenoff, A. (2016, November 7). *7 Sex toys that will give a boost to an older woman's libido.* HuffPost50. Retrieved from www.huffpost.com/

Brown, J.M., Hess, K.L., Brown, S., Murphy, C., Waldman, A.L.,& Hezareh, M. Intravaginal practices and risk of bacterial vaginosis and candidiasis infection among a cohort of women in the United States. *Obstetrics and Gynecology.* 2013;121(4):773-780. doi: 10.1097/AOG.0b013e31828786f8

Burns, J. (2016, July 15). *How the 'niche' sex toy market grew into an unstoppable $15B Industry.* Retrieved from Forbes.expo-founders-talk-15b-

CBS News. (2010, December 30). *Alabama Sex Toy Drive-thru Business on the Rise.* Retrieved from https://www.cbsnews.com/news/alabama-sex-toy-drive-thru-business-on-the-rise/

Center for Sexual Pleasure and Health. (2020). Retrieved from https://thecsph.org

Chatel, A. (2018, September 24). *9 Things To Know About Dildo Use Across the United States.* Bustle. Retrieved from https://www.bustle.com

Chen, L. (2020, October 19). *China's millennials stimulate $15 billion sex toy market.* The Jakarta Post. Retrieved from thejakartapost.com

Comella, L. (2017). *Vibrator Nation. How feminist sex-toy stores changed the business of pleasure.* Durham, NC. Duke University Press.

Comella, L. (2018, August 7). *20 years later, how the 'sex and the city' vibrator episode created a lasting buzz.* Forbes. Retrieved from https://www.forbes.com/

Cunha, A.R., Machado, R.M., Palmeira-de-Oliveira, A., Martinez-de-Oliveira, J., Das Neves, J., & Palmeira-de-Oliveira, R. Characterization of commercially available vaginal lubricants: A safety perspective. *Pharmaceutics* 2014, (6):530-542. Retrieved from https://doi.org/10.3390/pharmaceutics6030530

Dangerous Lilly. (2015, May 31) *Yes, it's the cordless rechargeable-magic wand.* Retrieved from http://dangerouslilly.com/2015/05/

DePree, B. (2013). Vibrators, your practice, and your patients' sexual health: Why you should be offering vibrators and related devices to your patients within your established practice, and options for doing so. *OBG Management.* April, 25(4), 41-49. Retrieved from https://cdn.mdedge.com/files/s3fs-public/Document/September-2017/2504OBG_DePree.pdf

Dezzutti, C.S., Brown, E.R., Moncia, B., Russo, J., Cost, M., Wang, L., & Rohan, L.C. (2012). Is Wetter Better? An Evaluation of Over-the-Counter Personal Lubricants for Safety and Anti-HIV-1 Activity. *PLOS ONE* 7(11). https://doi.org/10.1371/journal.pone.0048328

DiDomizio, N. (2015, August 25). This sex toy is busting myths about straight male sexuality. *Mic.* Retrieved from www.mic.com

Dodge, B., Schick,V., Herbenick, D., Reece, M., Sanders, S.A., & Fortenberry, J.D. (2014). Frequency, reasons for, and perceptions of lubricant use among a nationally representative sample of self-identified gay and bisexual men in the United States. *Journal of Sexual Medicine*; 11(10): 2396-2405. doi: 10.1111/jsm.12640

Edwards, D., & Panay, N. (2016). Treating vulvovaginal atrophy/genitourinary syndrome of menopause: how important is vaginal lubricant and moisturizer composition? *Climacteric,* 19(2), 151-161. doi.org/10.3109/13697137.2015.1124259

Ersner-Hershfield, R., & Kopel, S. A. (1979). Group treatment of preorgasmic women: Evaluation of partner involvement and spacing of sessions. *Journal of Consulting and Clinical Psychology.* 47(4), 750-759. doi.org/10.1037/0022-006X.47.4.750

Felicity. (2020, January 14). *The most realistic dildo: Expert ranking.* Phallophile Reviews. Retrieved from https://phallophilereviews.com/the-most-realistic-dildo-expert-ranking/

Frank, C. (2014, August 6). *9* Insane facts about sex dolls. *Cosmopolitan.* Retrieved from https://www.cosmopolitan.com/sex-love/news/a29834/amazing-facts-about-sex-dolls/

Frederick, D.A., Lever, J., Gillespie, B.J., & Garcia, J. (2017). What Keeps Passion Alive? Sexual Satisfaction is Associated with Sexual Communication, Mood Setting, Sexual Variety, Oral Sex, Orgasm, and Sex Frequency in a National U.S. Study, *The Journal of Sex Research*, 54:2, 186-201. doi: 10.1080/00224499.2015.1137854

Garnick, M. (Ed.). (2017). *2017 Annual Report on Prostate Disease.* Boston, Massachusetts: Harvard Medical School.

Gorbach, P.M., Weiss, R.E., Fuchs, E., Jeffries, R.A., Hezerah, M., Brown, S., & Cranston, R. (2012). The slippery slope: lubricant use and rectal sexually transmitted infections: A newly identified risk. *Sexually Transmitted Diseases*: 39 (1). 59-64. doi: 10.1097/OLQ.0b013e318235502b

Goldman, A. (2003). *Panic in bedrooms as magic wand, cadillac of vibrators disappears.* Observer. Retrieved from Observer.com

Gottlieb, S. (2004). Frequent ejaculation may be linked to decreased risk of prostate cancer. *British Medical Journal,* 328 (7444), 851. Retrieved from https://www.ncbi.nlm.nih.gov/pmc/articles/PMC387502/

Glickman, A. (2015, August 26). *How LELO is helping guys reach uncharted orgasmic territory.* Refinery29. Retrieved from https://www.refinery29.com/

Grand View Research. (2019, August). *Personal lubricant market analysis by type (water-based, silicone-based, oil-based), by distribution channel (e-commerce, drug stores), by regions, competitive insights, and segment forecasts, 2019-2026.* Retrieved from https://www.grandviewresearch.com/industry-analysis/personal-lubricant-market

Grand View Research. (2021, January). *Sex toy market, share & trends analysis report by type (male, female) by distribution channel (e-commerce, specialty stores, mass merchandizers), by region, and segment forecasts, 2021-2028.* Retrieved from https://www.grandviewresearch.com/industry-analysis/sex-toys-market

Gum, W. (2019, February 28). *Prostate massage for seniors: Know its benefits.* [Web log comment]. The Daily Dog. Retrieved from https://thedailydogblog.com/prostate-massage-for-senior-know-its-benefits/

Gunter, J. (2020, April 5). Sex and the corona virus: closeness in dark days. *New York Times.* p.4.

Gurley, G. (2015, May). Is this the dawn of the sexbots? *Vanity Fair.* Retrieved from https://archive.vanityfair.com/

GVibe. (2017, August 29). *Materials for sex toys: silicone and ABS-plastics.* Retrieved from https://gvibe.com/blogs/sex-blog/materials-for-sex-toys-silicone-and-abs-plastics

Hart, M. (2020). Guide to Sex Lubes. [Web blog#1]. Blissful Cherry. Retrieved from https://blissfulcherry.com/

Herbenick, D., Reece, M., Sanders, S.T., Dodge, B., Ghassemi, A., & Fortenberry, J.D. (2009). Prevalence and characteristics of vibrator use by women in the United States: Results from a nationally representative study. *Journal of Sexual Medicine,* 6:1857-1866. https://doi.org/10.1111/j.1743-6109.2009.01318.x

Herbenick, D., Reece, M., Sanders, S.T., Dodge, B., Ghassemi, A., & Fortenberry, J. D. (2010). Women's vibrator use in sexual partnerships: Results from a nationally representative survey in the United States. *Journal of Sex and Marital Therapy,* 36(1):49-65. https://doi.org/10.1080/00926230903375677

Herbenick, D., Reece, M., Hensel, D., Sanders, S., Jozkowski, K., & Fortenberry, J.D. (2011). Association of lubricant use with women's sexual pleasure, sexual satisfaction, and genital symptoms: A prospective daily diary study. *Journal of Sexual Medicine,* 8:202-212. https://doi.org/10.1111/j.1743-6109.2010.02067.x

Herbenick, D., Reece, M., Schick, V., Sanders, S.A., & Fortenberry, J.D. (2014). Women's use and perceptions of commercial lubricants: Prevalence and characteristics in a nationally representative sample of American adults. *Journal of Sexual Medicine,* 11(3): 642-652. doi: 10.1111/jsm.12427

Hess, A. (2015, February 4). There was a dildo on Broad City Abbi wore it. *Slate.* Retrieved from Slate.com

Hochberger, L. (2016, May 11). 11 Potentially harmful materials to look out for when you're buying sex toys. *Elite Daily.* Retrieved from https://www.elitedaily.com/life/harmful-materials-sex-toys/1490258

Jozkowski, K., N., Herbenick,D., Schick,V., Reece M., Sanders, S.A., & Fortenberry, J.D. (2013). Women's perceptions about lubricant use and vaginal wetness during sexual activities. *Journal of Sexual Medicine,* 10(2):484-492. doi. 10.1111/jsm.12022

Kassel, G. (2019, July 22). *How to introduce sex toys into your relationship: because whipping out a dildo in the heat of the moment is definitely "not" the way to do.* Retrieved from Shape.com

Kunst, A. (2019, December 20). Sex toy ownership of female consumers in the U.S. by type 2017. *Statistica.* Retrieved from https://www.statista.com/forecasts/744530/sex-toy-ownership-of-female-consumers-in-the-us-by-number-of-toys

Lanquist, L. (2018, March 15). *Clean your sex toys so you can use them safely.* Retrieved from Self.com

Languist, L (2020, May 12). A beginner's guide to every kind of vibrator. Retrieved from sheKnows.com

Laumann, E.O., Paik, A., & Rosen, R.C. (1999). Sexual dysfunction in the United States: Prevalence and predictors. *Journal of American Medical Association,* 281(6):537-544. doi: 10.1001/jama.281.6.53

LELO (2015, October 21). *Which countries and which US cities buy the most prostate massagers?* [Web log comment]. Retrieved from https://www.lelo.com/sites/default/files/PR_LOKI_WAVE.pdf

Leitzmann, M.E., Platz, E.A., Stampfer, M.J., Willett, W.C., & Giovannucci, E. (2004). Ejaculation frequency and subsequent risk of prostate cancer. *Journal of American Medical Association,* 291 (13): 1578-1586. doi: 10.1001/jama.291.13. 1578

Lieberman, H. (2017). *Buzz *A stimulating history of the sex toy.* New York, London: Pegasus.

Lieberman, L., & Cuadrado, M. (2005). Psycho-sensory comparative testing of three different types of vibrators (hitachi wand, prelude, and Eroscillator used as sensual massagers). [Unpublished raw data. City University of New York]. Retrieved from https://eroticmassagers.com/pages/cuny-study-eroscillator

Lloyd, E. A. (2006). *The case of the female orgasm: Bias in the science of evolution.* Cambridge, Massachusetts, London, England: Harvard University Press.

Maragakis (2020). *Coronavirus (COVID-19): Frequently Asked Questions.* John Hopkin Hospital. Retrieved from hopkinsmedicine.org

McBride, K., & Fortenberry, J.D. (2010). Heterosexual anal sexuality and anal sex behaviors: A review. *The Journal of Sex Research,* 47:2-3,123-136.
https://doi.org/10.1080/00224490903402538

Melancon, S. (2019, February 10). *Dangerous sex toy materials 101.* [Web log: post]. Sex Toy Collective. Retrieved from https://sextoycollective.com/blog/

National Council of Aging. (n.d.). *Fall prevention facts.* Retrieved from https://www.ncoa.org/article/get-the-facts-on-falls-prevention

National Survey of Sexual Health and Behavior (2010). Indiana University. School of Public Health. Bloomington, Indiana.

Price, J. (2013, January 31). *Tenga flip hole and 3-D sculpted ecstasy: Sex toys for men.* Retrieved from https://joanprice.com/

Rawls, P. (2007, October 2). High court leaves Ala. sex toy ban intact. *National Law Journal* Retrieved from https://www.oklahoman.com/article/3138400/court-leaves-ala-sex-toy-ban-intact

Reece, M., Rosenberger, J.G., Schick, V., Herbenick, D., Dodge, B., & Novak, D.S. (2010). Characteristics of vibrator use by gay and bisexually identified men in the United States. *The Journal of Sexual Medicine,* 7(10):3467-76. doi: 10.1111/j.1743-6109.2010.01873x.PMID 20561168

Reece, M., Herbenick, D., Schick, S.A., Sanders, S.A., & Fortenberry, J.D. (2014). Men's use and perceptions of commercial lubricants: prevalence and characteristics in a nationally representative sample of American adults. *Journal of Sexual Medicine,*11(5):1125-1135. https://doi.org/10.1111/jsm.12480

Reece, M., Herbenick, D., Sanders, S.A., Dodge, B., Ghassemi, A., & Fortenberry, J.D. (2009). Prevalence and characteristics of vibrator use by men in the United States. *Journal of Sex Medicine,* 6(7):1867-74. doi: 10.1111/j.1743-6109.2009.01290

Reid, C. (2019, August 27). *The number of 'digisexuals' is expected to surge-but who are the people who make sex dolls?* LadBible. Retrieved from www.ladbible.com/community/weird-interesting-number-of-digisexuals-is-expected-to-surge-as-the-tech-gets-better-20171129

Ruby, M. (2015, December 14). *Dangerous sex toy materials.* Miss Ruby Reviews. Retrieved from https://missrubyreviews.com

Ryder, R. (2013). *Toxic sex toys- what to know before you buy.* [Online forum: comment]. Reddit. Retrieved from Reddit.com

Schick, V., Herbenick, D., Rosenberger, J.G., & Reece, M. (2011). Prevalence and characteristics of vibrator use among women who have sex with women. *Journal of Sexual Medicine,* 8(12): 3306-3315. https://doi.org/10.1111/j.1743-6109.2011.02503.x

Schreiber, K. (2017, May 27). *How sex toys impact relationships. Do they always increase satisfaction?* Psychology Today. [Online forum: post]. Retrieved from https://www.psychologytoday.com/us/blog

Silicon Wives. (nd). *Silicon Luxury Sex Dolls.* Silicon Wives. Retrieved from https://www.siliconwives.com

Silver, M. (2015, September 15). The benefits of prostate massages. *Sydney Morning Herald.* Retrieved from Smh.com.au

Smith, K. (2018, April 17). *What to do if you want to use sex toys with your partner, but they don't.* Retrieved from sheknows.com

Speiser, L. (2020, December 30). *Local homegrown New York retailers voted romantic depot best in 2020 by AVN.* Retrieved from World.einnews.com

Sperling, D. (2014), August 15). *Reduce your risk for prostate cancer.* Retrieved from https://sperlingprostatecenter.com/massage-prostate-health-makes-great-combo/

Stabile, E. (2013, July 12). Commentary. Getting the government in bed: regulating the sex toy industry. *Berkeley Journal of Gender, Law & Justice,* 28 (161). 161-184. https://lawcat.berkeley.edu/record/1125576?ln=en

Street, S. (2009, September 5). *The eroscillator: Leading a revolutionary movement.* AVN. Retrieved from https://avn.com

Steig, C. (2020, March 20). *How to clean your sex toys-because, yes, you have to do that.* [Web log comment]. Refinery29. Retrieved from www.refinery29.com

Stubbs, K.R. (1993). *The Essential Tantra: A modern guide to sacred sexuality.* Jeremy P. Tarcher/Penguin, NY.

Thorn, K. (2020, March 12). *Your Top 5 Questions about the Benefits of Prostate Massage Answered.* LELO.com. Retrieved from https://www.lelo.com/blog/five-questions-benefits-prostate-massaging/

United States Consumer Product Safety Commission. (2019, November 26). *Phthalates business guidance & small entity compliance guide.* Retrieved from cpsc.gov

Vargas-Cooper, N. (2013, May 3). *Deep inside the biggest little dildo factory in America.* BuzzFeed. Retrieved from buzzfeed.com

World Health Organization. (2012). *Use and procurement of additional lubricants for male and female condoms: WHO/UNFPA/FHI360: advisory note.* Retrieved from https://apps.who.int/iris/bitstream/handle/10665/76580/WHO_RHR_12.33_eng.pdf?sequence=1

Acknowledgments

No project like this is ever done alone. Thanks to the readers of my early drafts Evelyn Apter, Dawn Da Costa Wade, Linda Fuchs, Joshua Kaufman, and Gloria Keller. My appreciation to Julia Drelich for the illustrations. Special thanks to Ray Bossik for the title and book cover, to Elaine Bossik for the back cover and guidance, to the editor, Glenn Bossik, and to Jennifer Lyons for the interior design.

About the Author

Brenda Dressler, PhD, Human Sexuality and HIV/AIDs Prevention Educator is a visiting professor and consultant at Touro College in NYC. She is the author of seven HIV/AIDs prevention education curricula which are used in schools in forty-eight states.

Dr. Dressler was awarded ten research grants and wrote numerous research articles. She conducted workshops on child sexual abuse prevention at the Hebrew University in Israel and on HIV/AIDS prevention education at Kampala University, primary and secondary schools, and HIV/AIDS Treatment Centers in Uganda.

After retiring from Touro College at age 70, Dr. Dressler began conducting workshops and podcasts for older adults on the benefits of sexual activity and the prevention of sexually transmitted infections (STIs). Dr. Dressler is listed in Who's Who and received the Albert Nelson Marquis Lifetime Achievement award in 2019 for outstanding contributions to her profession.

CPSIA information can be obtained
at www.ICGtesting.com
Printed in the USA
JSHW041238101221
21131JS00005B/12

9 780578 888132